The Landscape of Gloucestershire

The
Landscape
of
Gloucestershire

Alan Pilbeam

TEMPUS

First published 2006

Tempus Publishing Limited
The Mill, Brimscombe Port,
Stroud, Gloucestershire, GL5 2QG
www.tempus-publishing.com

British Library Cataloguing in Publication Data.
A catalogue record for this book is available from the British Library.

ISBN 0 7524 3602 3

Typesetting and origination by Tempus Publishing Limited
Printed in Great Britain

Contents

Prologue:
view from the hill

The term 'landscape' usually refers to an area of land that is viewed, or that is represented in a painting or photograph. Often it suggests natural scenery but it may be applied also to a built-up and an industrial area – we refer to an urban landscape and an industrial landscape. In this book we take its broadest general meaning and consider all that is visible as we look at the county's scenery. We ask how it has come to be as it is, and what is the significance of what we see. There are different levels of explanation we can give in answer to these questions and here we will be concerned more with the 'how' than the 'why'. The latter is a more demanding question, whether we are considering creation by God or by man, and we may not avoid it simply because of its difficulty. For landscapes do express the values of those who have created them and landscapes change as values change. Sometimes there is strong resistance to these changes and relics of old landscapes become fossilised in the new; at other times change is rapid and all evidence of the past is quickly obliterated. Some landscapes also have symbolic meanings, while others are purely functional. We will touch on each of these issues in passing but our main concern is with the landscapes we can see and how they have come about.

To introduce the various elements of landscape it will help if we go to one of the well-known viewpoints in the county and for a while scan the scene. There are many suitable places for this because the land rises by roughly 200m on either side of the Severn valley and from both its eastern and western edges the views are extensive. Plump Hill or Littledean Hill on the west and Dover's Hill, Cleeve Hill, Leckhampton Hill, Crickley Hill, Painswick Beacon, Haresfield Beacon or Coaley Peak on the east, are all appropriate viewpoints and, allowing for a short walk, are easily accessible to the motorist. The summits of May Hill and of Barrow Hill near Arlingham give even greater vistas because from them we can see far in all directions.

The viewpoint chosen here is less frequented than the famous ones and is at the top of Shurdington Hill (*colour plate 1*). The photograph was taken on a January morning after a cold night; hoar frost still covers the grass. The northerly airstream was being warmed as it moved southwards across the country so the relatively low levels of water vapour in the cold polar air did not lead to condensation and cloud formation, and because the air was becoming unstable, its turbulence dispersed any dust or carbon particles in the lower atmosphere. As a consequence distant features may be seen with unusual clarity.

The land slopes steeply down the scarp face of the Cotswolds in the foreground. We shall see later how the underlying geology of the slope is masked by a covering of small solifluction hummocks, where in periglacial conditions slabs of limestone have slid down from the outcrop at our feet. Less than 100m to our left is an overgrown quarry from which blocks of oolitic limestone have been cut for some of the buildings at the foot of the slope. The land on the hill has been grazed for centuries by sheep and cattle so there has been some check on the spread of hawthorn scrub and brambles, and many characteristic Cotswold flowers flourish. Because sheep nibble so close to the ground, plants with rosette leaves and growth tips near ground level are able to survive, while those with growth tips at higher levels are checked. Foxes and rabbits are common on the hill. Where water seeps out at the surface lower down the slope, the wet ground is wooded with willow, alder and ash trees with the occasional oak, sycamore and horse chestnut. There is also a rare group of Black Poplars. In the 1880s on this hillside the youthful Edward Wilson developed his skills in observing, sketching and painting wild life, a skill later used on his polar expeditions.

A line of trees in the left foreground marks the edge of Greenway Lane. In the eighth century St Peter's Abbey, now Gloucester Cathedral, acquired sheep pastures at Pinswell near Upper Coberley, and Greenway Lane linked these pastures with the manor of Badgeworth which also belonged to the abbey. The lane was a Saxon sheep drove road. It is not the oldest man-made feature of the area, for within 300m of our viewpoint is a well-preserved Neolithic long barrow (*50*), just below it is the site of a Roman villa (*51*) and a short distance beyond is the intensively studied Iron Age camp on Crickley Hill.

The group of buildings in the left foreground includes the Greenway Hotel. This fine early seventeenth-century country house with its gables and finials, and its mullioned and transomed windows, has a frontage which is almost unchanged from the engraving by Jan Kip in Sir Robert Atkyns' *Ancient and Present State of Gloucestershire*. The house was built for William Lawrence whose formal garden has now gone, but a few mature oak trees date from the time of the Lawrences' garden.

On either side of the A46, which runs across the foot of the escarpment and was turnpiked in 1819, are spreads of wind-borne glacial sands known as Cheltenham Sands. These give well-drained, fertile soils and have been used for market gardening for many decades. The glasshouses and nurseries are modern developments from these earlier activities. There is also a small sandpit to the left just beyond the main road.

Most of the nineteenth-century houses along the A46 were built for shop owners and other workers in nearby Cheltenham, and the modern housing here is also largely of a dormitory nature.

The underlying rock of the flat lowland in the middle distance is Lias Clay. It produces a heavy soil, often waterlogged in winter and cracked in summer. The farmland is mainly used for permanent pasture but there are some arable fields growing cereals and root crops, as is indicated by the large field showing exposed soil near the foot of Churchdown Hill. Formerly, much more land was cultivated and many of the pasture fields show the shallow corrugations of ridge and furrow. Most enclosure here was in the early nineteenth century and the majority of hedges bounding the rectangular or square fields date from this time. A few hedges are much older and may have eight or more different species of shrub in them, so indicating their greater age.

We may notice again the large irregularly-shaped arable field in the left middle distance. This field preserves the shape of the former Badgeworth Wood. It was a medieval wood and is marked on Isaac Taylor's one-inch map of Gloucestershire of 1777, being then surrounded by open fields which included Bentham Field to the left and Bradlington Field to the right. Like so many ancient woods it has been cleared for farmland but its former outline is shown in the pattern of field boundaries. Beyond it the M5 motorway lies hidden in a cutting.

Churchdown Hill to the right of the view rises to 154m and is one of many outliers of the Cotswolds. As the escarpment receded, places where the rock was slightly more resistant, or which were positioned between the small tributary streams draining into the Severn, were left outstanding. The hill is partly capped by a layer of Marlstone, a more resistant sandy limestone, which often forms a ledge along the scarp face of the Cotswolds. On the right-hand edge of the hill is St Bartholomew's church. Churches are often on the highest ground of a village but this is an extreme example. The place name 'Churchdown Hill' is interesting too. If its origin is Saxon and refers to a church, it is to an earlier one than the present Norman church and gives a simple tautology – 'church, on a hill (dun), on a hill'. If, however, the origin is cruc from the Welsh crug, its meaning is essentially 'hill, hill, hill' each component of the name coming from the language spoken by successive settlers.

Beyond Churchdown Hill, to the left, is the city of Gloucester, with its magnificent cathedral tower visible for miles around and its architecturally less distinguished eleven-storey concrete Royal Gloucestershire Hospital. Around its periphery are modern buildings for industry, commerce and offices.

In the distance we can discern the rounded outline of May Hill rising to 296m with its landmark clump of pine trees. Although there has been some recent planting of Scots pines here, the earlier ones date from 1887 and commemorate the Golden Jubilee of Queen Victoria. However, Francis Witts mentions a view of May Hill with a plantation on its summit in an entry in his diary for 26 August 1820.

Further on, after a series of low escarpments the land rises again to the northern fringe of the Forest of Dean and beyond to the outline of distant hills in Wales.

It is a morning view. In the evening when the sun is setting the silhouette of Hay Bluff and the Brecon Beacons may be seen more clearly, and in January these are likely to have a covering of snow on their summits. The view is extensive and sometimes breathtaking, but we could go to any of the viewpoints mentioned at the beginning of this introduction and, in a similar way, enjoy the vista and identify some of the distinctive features in the landscape before us. However, for a fuller appreciation of what we are looking at we need to consider in more detail the various elements that make up the landscape, and to this we now turn. In each of the following chapters we shall consider one of the main components of the landscape, beginning with its geology.

I

Cliffs and cuttings, mines and quarries

Gloucestershire has an impressive variety of sedimentary rocks, a variety that is simplified in F.W. Harvey's reference to 'forest and vale and high blue hill'. This expresses the basic threefold geological division of the county.

Rocks which are exposed at the land surface vary in their hardness, and so in their resistance to the processes of weathering and erosion. They also vary in their permeability, and so in the amount of surface drainage that has developed on their exposures; in their thickness, and so in the area of their outcrops; and in the degree of distortion from their original horizontal layering by the subsequent earth movements of folding and faulting. These variations account for many of the relief features of our landscape. Generally, the harder rocks, or those with little surface drainage, form higher ground and the softer rocks, with more abundant streams, give low ground. In addition to these structural details the rocks vary in the quality of soil they produce, which affects their natural plant communities and their agricultural potential, and the building materials derived from them. Thus the major geological outcrops have their own distinctive landscapes in which the visual components of the landscape are integrated by the underlying rocks. The contrasts between Forest, Vale and Cotswold are essentially geological, and we shall consider each in turn.

The Forest of Dean, which looks like a plateau when seen from a distance, has a basin structure rather like a stack of saucers. The structure is asymmetrical with

1 The Buck Stone, a large block of Quartz Conglomerate near Staunton

a steeper dip of rocks on the east, and is distorted by faults and internal folds. Two very resistant rocks form the rim of the Forest. The outer one, older and lower, is of Quartz Conglomerate. This is a relatively thin layer of rock consisting of a coarse sandy matrix, in which are set pebbles of quartz and other stones. It outcrops as a cliff-like feature often associated with massive isolated blocks, such as the Suck Stone and Buck Stone (*1*) near Staunton. It has been used as a building material for walls, but because of its composition and hardness it cannot be so easily shaped as most building stones. However, there has been a local market for it in millstones and the troughs and runners of cider mills.

Inside the rim of Quartz Conglomerate, and higher, is another of Dolomite. This is a hard grey limestone and has been quarried all round the Forest. Most of the steep approach roads were bordered by Dolomite quarries and its principal use has been as a roadstone and for burning in lime kilns. The 'steep and lofty cliffs' of Wordsworth's 'Lines above Tintern', which are found along the Wye Valley near Symonds Yat, are of Dolomite, as is the Yat Rock itself. So too are the cliffs beside the Wye at Wintour's Leap (*2*). The huge modern roadstone quarries south-west of Coleford are also cut in Dolomite.

In the upper layers of Dolomite is the Crease Limestone, and within this are pockets of haematite iron ore. These ores have been mined for centuries. Originally

2 Cliffs of the hard Dolomite limestone rising above the muddy tidal water of the River Wye near Wintour's Leap

only the surface exposures were worked, and the unevenly trenched and pitted areas where the veins of ore were mined are known as scowles. Scowles are found in several places in the Forest and are particularly well seen in the north-west of Lydney Park and in Puzzle Wood near Coleford (*colour plate 2*). There is usually a weird assemblage of ferns, mosses and twisted and gnarled yew trees clinging to the exposed rock edges. Old yew trees, conspicuous by their dark foliage in winter, often indicate where these early mines are to be found along the limestone outcrops. As the demand for iron ore increased, both for the blast furnaces that were set up in the Forest and for export from the river ports along the Severn and Wye, larger mines were opened, particularly along the eastern edge near Cinderford. Huge caverns were dug out, described by later miners as 'old men's workings'. These caverns, or 'churns', have been discovered while developing the nineteenth-century mines of Edge Hill, St Annal's, Buckshaft and Shakemantle in the east of Dean near Cinderford, and the Old Sling and Easter mines near Coleford in the west. The highest production figures were reached in the 1870s and an estimated total of 10 million tons of ore has been extracted. By the end of that century most mines had closed and parts of the extensive cave system produced by mining are now generally flooded. A walk along Edge Hills, north of Collafield, passes some of the awesome fenced-off mine shafts, and amid the birdsong of the larch and pine plantations it is difficult to imagine the heavy labour that once went on here. All the mine buildings have been demolished, but a visit to Clearwell Caves gives an impression of the underground workings, and the famous miner's brass in Newland church portrays the clothes and tools of an early miner.

Within the Dolomite rim are the Coal Measures which make up the interior dissected plateau of the Forest. There are several series of coal seams, mostly thin, and separated by much thicker layers of sandstone and shale. Because the seams outcrop towards the edge of the Forest, as with iron mining, early coal mining also occurred here and the free miners followed the seams underground until flooding became too much of a problem. Many of the later mines were shaft mines and located in the valleys which cross the interior of the Forest. Large-scale shaft coal mining ceased in the 1960s although there has been some open-cast work more recently. The spoil tips have either been removed, or are masked by the natural regeneration of birch and by the planting of pine trees; any remaining mine buildings have been put to alternative uses. One or two free mines remain, as for example in Wimberry Slade (3) and Bix Slade. These are usually worked by two or three men, on a part-time basis, and produce coal for

3 A typical coal free mine. Traditionally a free miner had to be born in St Briavel's Hundred and work in a mine for a year and a day, then he could apply to the Gaveller, the local representative of the Crown, to open a small-scale drift mine such as this

4 Bixhead Quarry. This large quarry in Pennant Sandstone still produces stone for ornamental building purposes

domestic use and for power stations. They are drift mines and last for a few years with their collection of corrugated iron sheds, stacks of pit props, narrow gauge rails and trucks and heaps of graded coal. They leave scarcely a trace once mining ceases and the vegetation grows over the closed entrances to the mines. A disused mine in Howlers Slade is now open to the public, and from this some awareness of the working conditions of the free miners may be gained. The soil that has developed on the exposed Coal Measures is normally clayey, and well suited to growing oak trees. Ponds and damp places often indicate the coal outcrop. The strata of the Coal Measures also include the hard blue or grey, fine grained, Pennant Sandstone, which is quarried and sawn for ornamental purposes, and for many years has been used for prestigious construction work. It was used, for example, in Telford's Over Bridge at Gloucester. The massive quarries at Bixhead (*4*) and Cannop Hill have been worked for this stone, and the stone is sawn at the Forest of Dean Stone Company Works at the south end of Cannop ponds. Pennant Sandstone forms the major hill feature on the west side of the Cannop Brook.

Another source of building stone, particularly for churches and older houses, and which is associated with the Forest, is the Brownstone of the Old Red

Sandstone series. This outcrops to the east of the Forest rim and is seen in the conspicuous red quarries at Mitcheldean. It was used in building Speech House. This rock also weathers to produce a fertile soil, suitable for both agriculture and productive forestry. The line of rounded hills including Chestnuts Hill, which Leonard Clark compared to a giant's umbrella, Welshbury and Shapridge marks its outcrop.

To the east of these rocks is a very significant geological boundary zone consisting of a series of faults running north–south from the Malverns and known as the Malvern fault belt. Rocks of very different ages and characteristics outcrop either side of this zone.

The lowland of the Severn valley has a much simpler geological structure than the Forest and, apart from surface spreads of gravels, sands and alluvium, the underlying rock west of the river is mainly Keuper marl, now known as Mercia Mudstone, and east of the river is mainly Lias Clay. Both rocks are best seen in river cliffs along the Severn. The meandering river has cut into a low hill at Westbury to expose the Mercia Mudstone and the beds immediately above it, and into a similar hill on the other side at Fretherne to expose the Lias Clay.

5 Westbury Garden Cliff. The River Severn has cut into the red Mercia Mudstone of the cliff. Notice the green bands in the cliff face and at the far end slabs of Pullastra Sandstone come down to the water's edge

There are other river cliffs, for example at Wainlode and near Lydney, but these two are the most informative.

At Westbury Garden Cliff (5) the rocks dip north-eastwards at an angle of about nine degrees, and so we are able to see not only the reddish Mercia Mudstone and its bands and splashes of green where the iron compounds in the rock have been reduced, but also the thin outcrop of Rhaetic beds and the base of the Lias Clay. Apart from the bright colour of the cliff, an interesting feature is the accumulation of large slabs of rock at its upstream foot. These slabs formerly capped the hill and they show on their surfaces the ripple marks and worm casts of an early shore. They often sparkle with crystals of iron pyrite, and the small fossil remains of fish and reptiles may be found on their surfaces. It is possible to walk along the base of the cliff to view these stones – but beware of the incoming tide!

Lower down the river and on the opposite side near Fretherne is Hock Cliff (6). Here bands of Lias Limestone alternate with clay. This too is a cliff which is famous for fossils. In places Ammonites and Gryphea (the devil's toenail) are common in the clay bands of the cliff and the beautifully shaped stems of

6 Hock Cliff at Fretherne. Bands of Lias Clay and Lias Limestone alternate and many fossils are found in the clay here

Pentacrinus (the sea lily) may also be found. Again the mud can be treacherous. Lias Clay, which is blue-grey at depth, also contains larger fossils including those of Ichthyosaurus and some fine specimens of this reptile were found when cuttings were made for the M5 motorway. A well-worn example may be seen in the porch of Tredington church.

Rhaetic beds outcrop in a narrow resistant band close to the centre of the Severn valley and they make up the ridge along which the A38 approaches Tewkesbury from Combe Hill.

Most of the western scarp face of the Cotswolds and the slopes of its outliers, such as Churchdown Hill and Robinswood Hill, consist of sands and clays. In places where clay outcrops springs are common, and where the fine grained Marlstone outcrops a ledge is normally found midway up the slope. This is well seen on Robinswood Hill and along the scarp face between Dursley and Wotton. Most of the underlying geological details of the scarp face are masked by surface deposits which have been brought down from the top of the escarpment in periglacial times, as we shall consider in the next chapter.

The area of the Cotswolds is best delimited by the outcrops of oolitic limestone. At the simplest level Cotswold geology may be likened to a sandwich, with a thick bottom slice of Inferior Oolite, a very thin filling of Fuller's Earth, and a medium thickness top slice of Great Oolite. The strata dip gently to the south-east at a slope of one or two degrees, but as this is steeper than the slope of the surface, all three rock types are exposed in succession.

In detail the geology is more complex. Oolitic limestone is a stone often composed of small spherical particles of about the size of a pin head. Each particle has at its centre a grain of sand, or a fragment of shell, which is surrounded by concentric layers of calcium carbonate, rather like a hailstone in formation. The temperature, salinity and turbulence of the water, which enables calcium carbonate to be precipitated in this way, point to the origin of the limestone in a shallow tropical sea surrounded by desert. While the sediment was settling flexures occurred along N–S axes. More sediment accumulated in the hollows and the upfolds experienced erosion. This creates discontinuities in the beds. Where the layers wedge out it is only by fossil remains that one can identify strata of the same age. There has also been faulting along roughly E–W lines.

In terms of quarrying the most significant beds are those of freestone. This type of Oolite has few fossils and may be extracted in massive blocks along the well-defined joints and bedding planes. Old quarries for freestone occur along the top of the escarpment in the Inferior Oolite at Fish Hill above Broadway, Leckhampton (7), Painswick and in many other places, and account for the white scars that were once so conspicuous when the Cotswolds were viewed from the west. But the most famous freestone quarries were just north of the present

7 Quarry face in Inferior Oolite at Leckhampton, showing the vertical joints and horizontal bedding planes that separate the easily quarried blocks of freestone. Notice that the angle of the grassy slope at the top of the photograph corresponds to that of the scree in the foreground

A40 from Sherborne eastwards. Here the Taynton Stone of the Great Oolite has been mined and quarried for centuries and used not only in local buildings but transported by boat along the Thames to Oxford, Windsor and London. One notable quarry was behind the Inn For All Seasons at Barrington, from which stone for the Sheldonian Theatre in Oxford was obtained. The area is now an overgrown uneven waste but the mining levels once went far under the present road.

The colour of the Oolite when exposed to the weather varies through its content of ferric carbonate, and ranges from a lemon and silver-grey in the south of the Cotswolds, through amber, to what H.J. Massingham once described as its 'autumnal tawniness' in the north. In buildings it is seen at its best in a low evening sunlight.

Another important bed in the Great Oolite is that of Stonesfield Slate, named after the village in Oxfordshire where it has been quarried. This is a sandy, shelly, limestone which is fissile, i.e. it can be easily separated into thin layers. From this stone the traditional Cotswold roof slates have been cut. Stonesfield Slate has been brought to the surface by block faulting in several restricted localities such as north of Bisley at Througham, and at Naunton where it is still worked. Here the quarries are shallow and the land is restored for agricultural use once the stone has been extracted.

Fuller's Earth, which separates the Greater from the Inferior Oolite, is a calcareous mudstone which is soft and easily eroded. It accounts for the springs which are the principal site factor of many Cotswold villages, and the landslides and slumping along the sides of the Cotswold river valleys mark its outcrop.

At one time almost every Cotswold and scarp foot parish had its quarry both for local building purposes and for roadstone, but some of the more sought after masons preferred to bring stone from their own quarries. Valentine Strong, for example, brought stone from Taynton to build Lower Slaughter manor in the 1650s. Most of these quarries are now overgrown and on their weathered surfaces and scree slopes some of the more delicate calcareous flowers grow. These areas are also havens for wildlife. The quarries were small scale, worked by hand, and made limited visual impact on the landscape. There are, however, a few extensive and deep modern quarries which are worked by heavy machinery and which produce crushed stone for synthetic building blocks (*8*). Although they are largely screened by banks and trees from nearby view, they are often visible from a distance and their size and depth raise serious environmental concerns.

8 Daglingworth Quarry. One of several extensive and deep quarries on the Cotswolds which are largely hidden from view

The science of geology began in England with the work of William Smith, who came from Churchill in the Oxfordshire Cotswolds. He made many of his observations when engaged in canal digging. When railway cuttings were made through hilly country in the next century a more extensive sequence of rock exposures could be observed than along the canal routes, and the subject rapidly advanced. In the local area, although trees and scrub have often covered the sides of the cuttings after the lines were abandoned in the 1960s, geology interest groups still from time to time clear the more informative exposures. Two examples are north-west of the Roman villa at Chedworth and from Hampen through to Bourton-on-the-Water, where there are good sequences of rocks of the Great Oolite. Modern road construction has also produced cuttings in which the strata are exposed as, for example, along the A417 north of Cirencester.

In addition to the main threefold division of the county there is a smaller but still important and distinctive landscape associated with the line of the Malvern Hills. Many views from the Cotswolds looking west over the Severn valley have the Malverns as a backdrop, and to their south is the equally conspicuous rounded form of May Hill. The Silurian sandstones here are some of the oldest rocks in Gloucestershire, and they outcrop as the exposed interior of a dome-shaped structure. Younger rocks occur to the south-west of May Hill towards the Forest and among them, forming a slight escarpment, is a bed of Wenlock Limestone which has been quarried near Longhope. Here at Hobbs Quarries the rocks contain fossils of corals and crinoids and exhibit some of the finest fossilised reefs to be found in Britain.

Also in the north-west of the county is a small coalfield and former iron ore mining area near Newent. During the nineteenth century and also in earlier periods these supported a small scale local industry. Between Newent and the River Leadon at Pauntley is an outcrop of soft, very permeable, red sandstone, the Bromsgrove Sandstone. It is exposed in natural cliffs and road cuttings and produces an extremely dry soil, favourable to fruit growing and vineyards. And at Gorsley on the county border with Herefordshire another fine grained sandstone known as 'Gorsley stone' has been quarried, and this is the principal building stone for public buildings and older cottages in the area west and south of Newent.

Thus in geological terms the county is very rich, and the river cliffs along the Severn, the sides of the disused railway cuttings and the many old quarries and mines give us glimpses into its geology. The museums at Cheltenham and Stroud display specimens of the rocks and the associated fossils typical of their neighbourhoods, and these give us useful supplementary information. From these sources we have come to understand that rocks, originally formed in such diverse environments as seas, swamps and deserts, have been major contributors to the differences between our varied contemporary landscapes.

2

Landscapes produced by floods and frosts

In the present day the processes involved in the erosion and weathering of rocks in Gloucestershire, and therefore in giving shape to the land surface, generally operate very slowly and on those occasions when they are more rapid they tend to be very localised. Some examples will be mentioned briefly before we consider the far-reaching effects of the processes of the recent geological past. In very wet weather, clay slopes may become unstable and small-scale landslides occur. This happens especially on artificial slopes such as railway or motorway cuttings and embankments and where the natural angle of slope is greater than a few degrees, such as along the steep-sided tributary valleys of the Frome. The surface outcrops of Fuller's Earth and exposures of Lias Clay are vulnerable in this way. Occasionally farmers growing autumn sown cereals on steep slopes on the Cotswolds find that heavy rain in October and November, before the crop has spread to protect the soil, leads to soil erosion and that small stoney gulleys develop. These gulleys appear between the rows of plants and the fine grade eroded soil is also spread over the lower parts of the field (*colour plate 3*). Solution of limestone continues whenever acidic groundwater moves through the rock. This is especially the case in winter, and we have noticed that after snowfall the calcium bicarbonate content of streams draining the Cotswolds reaches its highest levels. Erosion also continues along the Severn when flood water from snow melt in Wales, or high tidal levels, saturates the banks and causes quite rapid

9 Sandhurst Hill from Woolridge Hill. This flat-topped hill is the remains of a former valley floor of the Severn. As with all the river terraces it is covered with a spread of pebbles

recession of those banks which are formed of soft material. In general, however, our rivers only have sufficient energy to erode their beds and banks on one or two days in the year. The slow downhill movement under gravity of loose rock fragments, demonstrated by turf rolls on grassy slopes and small screes at the foot of cliffs, is the most common process of land formation today. But past conditions were very different, and in this chapter we will consider the major effects of Ice Age melt water and severe frost on our landscapes.

In two important papers of 1899 and 1909 the American geographer W.M. Davis drew attention to the misfit rivers of the Cotswolds, where large valley meanders are now occupied by the meanders of much smaller rivers. These are well seen along the Coln north of Withington (10) and along the Windrush downstream of Naunton, but they are to be found in places along the courses of all the Cotswold rivers. Davis thought that river capture explained these features. His proposed explanation was that rivers originating in Wales flowed across what is now the Severn Valley and then down the dip slope of the Cotswolds into the Thames drainage system. Later, as the Severn developed, it beheaded these rivers, diverting the water of their upper courses towards the Bristol Channel and leaving the much reduced flow to form the smaller rivers of the Cotswold valleys. Although this was a coherent explanation, it was recognised that there were several problems with it. One was that it implied a vast amount of erosion had occurred in the Severn Valley, cutting it down to its present level, while the form of the Cotswold valleys had hardly changed at all during the same period of time. Another problem concerned the destination of the eroded material. This must have been deposited somewhere but the site was unknown. So this interesting explanation was eventually discounted, although geologists have continued to think that, in an earlier geological period, rivers from what is now Wales once crossed into the valley of the proto-Thames.

Recent research has reopened the subject. In some fields along the Evenlode valley south of Oddington, and at many sites along the Thames tributaries in Oxfordshire, the surfaces are covered with pebbles and other large fragments of rock. The pebbles are mainly formed of quartz and quartzite and they are derived from the erosion of Triassic conglomerates. Their source area is near Birmingham and they have been brought here by river. But today, between Birmingham and the Evenlode valley lies the River Avon and the Vale of Evesham and the only way a river could have brought this material is if it predated the formation of the Vale of Evesham. Some of this drift material has been dated to an age of around 450,000 years old and the implication drawn from this research is that the Vale of Evesham, and therefore the Vale of Gloucester, were excavated after this date which in geological time scales is very recent indeed. It corresponds to the last quarter of the Ice Age. Another recent discovery is that in the Celtic Sea to the south-west of Wales is a deep ocean trough which contains much eroded material. The thickness of the material is several hundred metres and its date at the base material is also about 450,000 years old. So it has been suggested that this deposit in the Celtic Sea consists of the eroded material from the Severn and Avon Valleys that has been excavated and transported by powerful flood water, which in turn resulted from the melting of the ice sheets in the Midlands towards the end of the Ice Age.

Both to the north and south of Gloucester are many low flat-topped hills. Two of the highest, Sandhurst Hill (9) and Woolridge Hill, on opposite sides of the Severn, are at roughly the same height above sea level at just above 80m. There are other flat topped hills at this level and many at lower levels. They have a slight sea ward slope, more so than the Severn itself, but this is not noticeable to the eye. The lane north of Maisemore crosses three of these levels like shallow steps, and similar step like features may be seen around Sandhurst, Hasfield and Tirley. They are river terraces, being the remains of the former valley floor of the Severn as, in six stages it cut down through the soft sedimentary rocks of its valley.

10 The Coln valley upstream of Withington. Notice the smooth curve of the valley floor and the intricate meander pattern of the recent course of the river before it was artificially straightened

On closer inspection of these flat surfaces we notice that they too are covered with pebbles (*colour plate 4*). Since most of the fields are used for arable crops the soil is frequently exposed and the pebbles are clearly visible. Some are of whitish quartz and brown quartzite, but there are also small black pebbles of igneous rock and occasionally more irregularly-shaped flints, as well as lumps of local Lias Limestone. The source of the black pebbles is the Malvern Hills and the flint has come from a far distant outcrop of chalk. The quartzite pebbles are the largest, with their long axis sometimes reaching 10cm. The pebble assemblages differ slightly from one terrace to another, both in their sizes and in their composition. This is significant because the size of the largest pebbles on each terrace indicates the transporting power of the river that brought them, and the differences in the types and frequency of pebbles on the terraces indicate changes in the area drained by these melt water floods. So it is possible to reconstruct changes in the discharge of the Severn, and its catchment area, from a study of the pebbles spread over its terraces. Also we notice many of the larger quartzite pebbles have been shattered. To split them requires a pressure of a mass of at least 500kg, and this demonstrates the severity of the frosts to which they have been subjected, either at their place of origin in the Midlands, or in transit to their present location.

   While the Severn Valley was being eroded in stages and the terraces formed, changes were also occurring on the Cotswolds. Around Moreton-in-Marsh deposits of Boulder Clay indicate that a late ice sheet reached as far south as this point, but most of the Cotswolds experienced periglacial, rather than glacial, conditions. The sub-surface rocks would have been permanently frozen and therefore impermeable to drainage water, while the surface layers of the rocks would have experienced seasonal alternations of freeze and thaw. During the summers ice and snow would have melted, thus saturating the surface layers and water would have had to flow over the land surface rather than infiltrating as it does today. As a result valleys were cut by this running water and the meandering patterns of these valleys, which today are dry, confirm this. However, other explanations of dry valleys have been suggested such as when layers of impermeable rocks, like Fuller's Earth, are breached by the downward cutting of a river. This would allow water, which once flowed over the surface, to infiltrate the permeable rocks below so giving dry surface conditions. But the periglacial explanation is likely in most cases. All the main Cotswold rivers have dry tributary valleys; they are common features. One of the best developed is a tributary valley of the Coln, north of Ablington (*11*). Here the meandering valley form has an asymmetrical cross section. One side is steeper than the

11 A dry valley near Ablington with an asymmetrical cross section

other with scars and turf rolls, indicating some present instability of the slope, in contrast to the gentler opposite side. In this example the steeper side was in the shade and remained frozen longer, while the sunny slope thawed out more readily and the saturated soil and loose rock on this side slumped to a gentler angle. Asymmetrical valleys are also quite common on the Cotswolds, but perhaps not as frequent as one might expect. Slopes on the Cotswolds are stable in present day conditions up to about 24 degrees, which is the angle of rest of loose fragments of limestone, as seen in the quarry screes at Leckhampton. Very steep slopes, such as at Swifts Hill near Slad, have this gradient. Cooper's Hill above Brockworth, where the annual cheese rolling chase takes place, is only slightly steeper at about 33 degrees.

Evidence of slumping or solifluction is also found along the face of the Cotswold escarpment. Many scarp slopes are covered with low grassy hummocks, perhaps a metre or two high and several metres long. Inside each hummock is a slab of oolitic limestone. These slabs have been split from the Inferior Oolite outcrop at the top of the escarpment by frost, and then have slid down the slope in periglacial conditions and come to rest at various levels. Subsequent weathering of the limestone and partial burial by soil creep has given them the

12 Solifluction hummock on the lower slope of the Cotswold escarpment. Inside each low mound is a slab of limestone which has slipped down from the top of the escarpment

rounded forms they display today. Their surfaces are drier and warmer than the surrounding slopes, and with their thin calcareous soil covering they support little islands of typical limestone vegetation. Plants such as hare bells, cowslips and salad burnet grow here, in contrast to the coarse grasses and taller vegetation of the clay soils surrounding them. They are well seen on Shurdington Hill (*12*). The geology of most steep, western slopes is masked by this unconsolidated material brought down by solifluction from higher up the slopes. It is referred to as 'Head' on the drift geological maps.

As mentioned earlier, the main Cotswold rivers occupy valleys which are larger than their present-day rivers warrant. The valleys were evidently cut when there were much greater discharges. In the case of the Coln valley between Andoversford and Withington one large valley meander is occupied by about ten meanders of the present river, or by traces in the meadows of meanders where the river once flowed (*10*). There are mathematical relationships between a river's discharge when it fills its bed and banks, the wave length of its meanders, and its width. If we calculate these relationships for the present-day rivers, it is possible to estimate the discharge and width of the rivers which have produced the large valley meanders. Bed widths of 30–40m are likely and this corresponds to some evidence from borings across the Coln valley, which have identified the river's former bed. So the question is raised as to how rivers so close together as the Churn, Coln, Windrush and Evenlode could have had such large discharges. Again periglacial melt water, as outlined above, is the most likely explanation. There have been other suggested explanations. One is that the overspill from a glacial lake north of the Cotswold escarpment created them. It is thought that this lake had a shoreline at 122m above sea level and in one or two cases, such as in the area of the upper Evenlode, the Cotswold escarpment is slightly below this. Most of the headwater areas of these Cotswold rivers are above this height. Other suggested explanations include more intense rainfall in the past i.e. greater than the infiltration capacity of the soil; greater annual rainfall totals, perhaps of the order of 7500mm which is ten times greater than that of the present; spring sapping along the valley sides and breaches in impermeable strata. Cotswold valleys have interested geographers for years and it is likely that more than one explanation has accounted for their forms.

Lower down the valleys some of this eroded material has been deposited. As the gradients become gentler the ability of the rivers to transport their loads is reduced and the gravel spreads of the Thames Valley have been the result. These deposits are now being extracted on a large scale, and the flooded gravel pits that are left form the basis of the Cotswold Water Park at South Cerney. Plans have been produced for a major recreation and conservation area here. Some parts have been developed and the lake area already exceeds the Norfolk Broads – another man-made lake system of a much earlier date – in size.

The Cotswold escarpment has been indented with valleys draining into the Severn and fronted by outlying hills, such as Robinswood and Churchdown Hills, which mark former positions of the scarp. In the south the valleys are steep-sided and several kilometres long – the 'bottoms' as in Ozleworth, Tyley and Waterley Bottoms. Further north are the 'combes', which are shorter and more rounded in plan, as in Witcombe and Harescombe. These too are likely to be associated with periglacial processes and in front of the embayments are gravel spreads of the excavated material. These spreads have good drainage and were chosen for the sites of early settlement as the line of villages along the old Roman road, Ermin Way, through Witcombe, Brockworth, Hucclecote and Barnwood indicates. They have also been exploited in the gravel pits at Frampton. There are also many 'combes' within the Cotswolds, along the sides of the main valleys. Some of these are probably nivation hollows where patches of snow and ice remained for longer periods; around and beneath them frost shattering, wetting and drying, and solution weathering of the rock eventually produced the deep, rounded hollows similar to those seen in mid-Wales. A fine example is to the east of Rooksmoor Mills in the Nailsworth valley (*13*).

13 A beautifully rounded combe on the east side of the Nailsworth valley – possibly a nivation hollow

14 The Suck Stone, a massive rock which was dislodged from the Quartz Conglomerate outcrop above in periglacial conditions

When the ice sheets occupying the Midlands retreated at the end of the Ice Age, finely ground rock flour was left on the surface. After it had dried out fine particles were picked up by the cold winds blowing away from the ice sheets. In sheltered locations some of this aeolian material was dropped and this has produced the fertile patches of well-drained, silty soil in the Cheltenham area, referred to in the chapter on village sites and known as 'Cheltenham Sands'.

There has been less research on the landforms of the Forest of Dean, but here too we expect to find evidence of periglacial processes. Most of the rocks here are harder and so are more resistant to weathering and erosion. When the Forest is viewed from the Cotswolds it appears to have a plateau surface at about 200m above sea level, sloping gently to the south. The meanders of the Wye originated on this surface and have been gradually entrenched as the river incised its gorge. As with all meanders on very gentle gradients there is a tendency for them to be cut off in times of flood. This has happened with the Wye at Newland, where a large abandoned meander is now drained by the two misfit Redbrook streams. Perhaps at some time in the future the same thing will happen at Symonds Yat. As with the Severn, during the down cutting of the Wye Valley relicts of former valley floors have been left as river terraces but they are more restricted in size than those of the Severn.

Solifluction has also occurred here. Blocks of rock from the two main outcrops of the Forest rim – Dolomite and Quartz Conglomerate – have been split off by frost and have slid down the slopes below. So the hillside above Mitcheldean is littered with blocks of Dolomite and Coppet Hill to the north of Symonds Yat can be seen to have a similar spread of Quartz Conglomerate rocks. The famous Suck Stone (*14*) near Staunton is another example of these dislodged rocks. These blocks have not weathered like the oolite and retain their original angular form.

As both the Severn and the Wye flow into the Bristol Channel they have been affected by the same sea-level changes. When sea levels fell during the glacial periods the rivers received new energy for erosion, enabling them to cut down to new base levels. Phases of down cutting and then of stability affected both rivers in the same way and their terraces therefore correspond. But sea-level changes have not been the only cause of renewed erosion. One effect of the removal of so much sedimentary rock from the Severn Valley has been an isostatic adjustment, which has caused an upward flexuring in the earth's crust. The upward tilting of the strata on either side of the valley has led to renewed river erosion. It has been noted earlier that the general slope south–eastwards of the Cotswold surface is less steep than the dip of the rocks; the recent incision of the upper valleys of the Cotswold rivers such as the Windrush near Temple Guiting, the Coln at Sevenhampton and the Churn at Cowley may be explained by this flexuring. The corresponding uplift on the western side of the Vale has probably followed the Malvern fault belt.

Much further investigation is necessary to unravel the recent landform history of the county. However, the evidence already considered shows how significant the last two million years have been and how important frosts and floods have been as landforming agents.

3

The trees and woods of the county

The northward migration of trees across southern England in post-glacial times has been demonstrated by pollen analysis. Pollen grains are the most durable parts of a plant and in waterlogged peat bogs and in very acidic soils they may survive for thousands of years. When allowance is made for the different amounts of pollen produced by the various tree species and for differences between the species in pollen mobility, it is possible to estimate the relative frequency of the different tree species in an area at successive stages in their re-colonisation of the land after the Ice Age. The general succession of trees in England has been of birch and pine, followed by elm, hazel and oak, then alder and lime, and finally beech. At the later stages non-tree pollen becomes common and this corresponds to the beginning of woodland clearance by early man.

It is unlikely that any of the original wild woods remain in Gloucestershire, although some woods on the steep slopes of the Wye Valley, such as Lady Park Wood, may contain traces of it. As early as Roman times the clearance of woodland would have been extensive, although woods were important to provide local sources of fuel for both domestic and industrial uses. The villa estates produced corn and wool for the urban market, and both products imply open country.

In the following Saxon period, when settlements were largely self-sufficient, most manors would have had their own woods from which timber for buildings and wood for fuel could be taken. But priority of land use for such a community would have been given to arable crops or cattle grazing, and woods would have been found where neither of these two uses was appropriate. So steeper slopes where ploughing was difficult, or land around springs where it was continually wet, or more remote areas towards the edges of the manor's territory were the preferred locations for such woods. Occasionally these ancient woods contain signs of earlier settlements such as the long barrow and tumulus at Withington, the Iron Age earthworks at Welshbury and High Brotheridge and a Roman villa at Spoonley. Since these features were associated with more open country, their occurrence within a wood indicates that the wood is a later development. Apart from their characteristic locations those ancient woods that have survived to the present day may be recognised by other features. Their outline is normally irregular, resulting from successive intakes, and the sinuous boundary around old trees often consists of an outer ditch and broadly rounded inner bank. Usually the old boundary trees have been pollarded in order to produce timber and keep the branches out of reach of browsing livestock. The interior of the wood is subdivided into blocks which were originally at different stages of coppicing, and these blocks are sometimes separated by earthen banks. Sunken trackways within the woods have been made by the age-long passage of the wagons and carts used to extract the timber. The woods have a greater variety of trees than those of more recent plantings, and may include such diagnostic species as the small leafed lime, field maple and hawthorn. The ground flora is also richer with the presence of shade-loving plants such as bluebells, wood anemone and dog's mercury, plants that take a long time to become established in the wild. Sometimes these plants indicate that what appears to be a new plantation was in fact woodland before the present trees were planted. A large insect population is also characteristic, and ancient woods have distinctive assemblages of spiders and snails. Frequently the wood is named after the nearby village. These, then, are the main indicators that a wood is old.

Sadly, many of medieval woods were gutted in the years immediately after the Second World War and either converted to farmland or partly replanted with conifers. Although this has resulted in ecological impoverishment, some of the other features may have survived. Thus with the aid of Isaac Taylor's map of 1777 – the first one-inch map of Gloucestershire – and some careful fieldwork, not only is it possible to identify some of these old woods but also to trace out the area they once occupied.

We begin our survey of the trees and woods of the county with those of the Forest of Dean. When viewed from a distance, or even within it from one of the ridges, the Forest appears to be largely coniferous woodland, whereas when travelling through it along one of the main roads it seems to consist mainly of mature oak trees. Both impressions are correct. The exposed ridges are planted with conifers and the roads are bordered by oaks, but the overall planting pattern is much more complex than this and is derived from centuries of management with varied and changing objectives.

The earliest management in Norman times was focused on the provision of cover and grazing for game, especially for deer and wild boar. Both St Briavel's Castle and Flaxley Abbey were used as bases for royal hunting, and a chimney on the Castle is in the shape of a hunting horn. Usually the numbers of deer in the Forest and the adjacent Highmeadow Woods have been controlled, although for a while in the mid-nineteenth century they were completely eliminated because of the moral temptation they presented to poachers! Fallow deer are still found in the Forest, particularly near Speech House, and there are often rumours of wild boar!

Oak has always been the main species of tree grown in the Forest. This is because of its use as a ship timber, for the Forest was the principal source of timber for the navy. But oak was also grown for use in buildings and mines, to supply charcoal for the iron industry, for domestic fuel and for its bark which was used in the tanneries. It had multiple uses, but ship timber and charcoal were historically the most important. The use of oak for naval ships ceased in 1874 but, because of their longevity, many trees originally planted for ship timber are still growing today. They were widely spaced in their planting to encourage branching so that 'crooks, bends and knees' could be provided for the ships. This spacing tended to cause rather low growth and also a vulnerability to wind damage. Also, from the early nineteenth century, some oaks were planted for scenic reasons and they still line many of the main roads through the Forest.

There are a few very old oak trees scattered across the Forest. Some of these date from the 1668 Forestry Act when concerns over the future supplies of ship timber, following extensive clear felling, led to the first planting programme. Before this, natural regeneration was allowed to replenish the woods. Several of these 'King Charles II Oaks' are in the Churchill Inclosure near Parkend. The famous 'Three Brothers' in the nearby Russells Inclosure, now reduced to one living specimen, also date from the seventeenth century. The other oaks in this inclosure south of Cannop ponds are typical of the early nineteenth-century plantings (*colour plate 5*). From them timber has recently been cut for the repair of HMS *Victory*. The dead trunk of the Crad Oak in Sallow Vallets is possibly the oldest remains of a standing tree (*15*). H.G. Nicholls, writing in 1858, said that the circumference of the spread of this tree was 90 yards.

Partly because oak is a native tree, as distinct from a recent introduction, there are hundreds of species of insect that feed on it. Some, such as the oak leaf roller

15 The decaying remains of the Crad Oak in Sallow Vallets, Forest of Dean. Once, the branches of this tree spread over the whole clearing. Several young trees have been planted to take its place

moth (*Tortrix viridiana*), from time to time completely strip the foliage but the trees quickly recover. The original sessile oak is less vulnerable to attacks of this sort than the pedunculate oak, which has been the variety normally planted. The insect population attracts many insectivorous birds. These include the pied flycatcher for which nest boxes are provided in the RSPB reserve at the Nags Head plantation – another 1813 planting.

Sowing acorns where the trees were required was not found to be a successful practice. Rooks, mice and voles ate the acorns and, even when germination had occurred, bracken and coarse grass overwhelmed the seedlings. So from the early nineteenth century nurseries were established to raise the trees and then the young trees were transplanted. An exception to this is the fine collection of oaks in Blakeney Hill Wood North near Blackpool Bridge – these were selected from natural regeneration. It is often possible to distinguish between plantation oak trees and those of natural succession because the trees of a plantation have similar characteristics of leaf shape, bark patterns, angles at which the branches join the trunk and autumn colouring, whereas the trees in natural woodland are more varied.

For the survival of the young trees it was necessary to enclose the plantations to prevent damage by the grazing animals of the commoners. So from the time of the 1668 Act cattle, sheep and pigs could be legally excluded from areas totalling up to 11,000 acres while the young trees were becoming established. Stone walls and earthen banks topped with gorse and hawthorn were constructed to keep the livestock out, a procedure not always welcomed by the local people. Remains of these enclosures may still be seen today.

Oak was not the only broadleaf tree to be planted. Sweet chestnut, a post-Roman introduction to Britain, is recorded in the Forest as early as 1237 growing along the old roads. Other records indicate that Chestnut Wood near Littledean was enclosed for coppicing in 1333, and the Vale of Castiard at Flaxley was long famous for its chestnuts. Chestnuts are still grown here, originally for their nuts but later to produce fence posts.

Beech also grows well in some areas of the Forest and is the second most important broadleaf tree here. It can normally overtop oak trees and so is often grown in oak plantations as a later underplanting. Its main use is for construction timber but in the past beech mast was an important food for pigs. Mature beech trees line the A4136 near Coleford and there are several notable beech areas.

The earliest conifer to be introduced was the Weymouth Pine, planted in 1781 in Sallow Vallets where a few descendants still grow. During the important 1808-18 planting programme it was realised that the Forest ridges were too exposed and the soil here was too thin for quality oak trees, and also that in some frost-prone hollows a nurse crop would help to protect the young trees. So European larch and Scots pine were introduced and planted both on the ridges and in the hollows. These grow more quickly than oaks, maturing after 40 to 60 years, and so not only provide shelter for the young hardwoods but also an intermediate source of income when they are cut. Douglas firs arrived in 1895 and the Japanese larch in 1912-15.

After the establishment of the Forestry Commission in 1919 and the beginning of its management of the Forest in 1924, a more extensive policy of conifer planting was adopted. In addition, the range of species was increased to include Corsican pine, Sitka spruce, Western red cedar, Lawson's cypress, Western hemlock, Grand fir and Californian redwood. The economics of modern forestry, with its demand for soft woods for pulping, and the need to secure a national reserve of timber dictated this trend, but extensive hardwood planting has continued. This is partly because conifers can be grown widely throughout Britain and suitable land for broadleaf trees is much more restricted, and partly because amenity planting has become increasingly emphasised in the management of the Forest. So depending on soil conditions, degree of exposure, previous crops and market projections, blocks of conifers fill in the areas between oak and beech woodland.

16 A typical view of the block planting of the Forest of Dean. Oak trees dominate the lower valley sides and conifers the ridges

17 A fine old oak tree near the Severn at Deerhurst. In most winters the meadows by the river are flooded and the deposits of silt brought by the water replenish the nutrients in the soil

Close planting often gives a gloomy atmosphere to these blocks and because the species of tree were introduced from distant parts of the world their associated wildlife is less abundant. However, conifers give visual diversity to the Forest landscape, particularly in winter when the woods would otherwise be bare, and they effectively screen industrial scars and hide the many users of the Forest tracks (*16*).

The scattered deciduous woods between the Forest and the Severn, such as those at Newent, Birdwood, Highnam and Ley, are outlying relics of the former forest which once occupied most of the land between the Severn and the Wye as far north as Newent. To the east of the Severn and below the Cotswold escarpment there is little woodland today, although early maps show named woods at Hatherley and Badgeworth (*colour plate 1*). The tall elms, which were once a major feature of the farmland in the Vale, were destroyed by the ravages of Dutch elm disease in the 1970s. Close to the Severn, south of Tewkesbury, are scattered specimens of fine mature oaks (*17*) and around Frampton a few Black Poplar trees grow by the Sharpness Canal. These poplar trees were once common on the wet low-lying meadows by the Severn and their rough, curved branches provided the framework for many of the cruck houses of the area,

18 A rare group of Black Poplar trees. Notice the large curved branches

but land drainage has largely destroyed their habitat (*18*). Pollarded willows are common and the Severn is frequently bordered by willow and alder trees.

On the Cotswolds the ancient woods fall into two groups. These are the extensive beech woods along the edge of the escarpment, especially from Witcombe to Dursley, and the mixed woods on the deeper soils of the hill sides bordering the river valleys further east.

Many of the beech woods are held or managed by conservation bodies such as English Nature, the National Trust and the Gloucestershire Trust for Nature Conservation. They consist of closely planted beech trees, which on maturity produce tall straight boles, with an understorey of yew, holly and box, but both ash and sycamore spread quickly unless checked. Some mature trees were the shoots from coppice stools which were last cut before the First World War. The dense shade, deep, slowly decaying litter and the shallow rooting system of the trees restrict the ground flora to strongly growing plants that flower before the leaf canopy has developed. Fine displays of wood anemones, bluebells and ramsons are common in these woods; ivy, dog's mercury and lords–and–ladies give early greenery. Stinking and green hellebores, spurge laurel and occasionally herb paris may also be seen. Sunlight on the bright green beech leaves in spring, or illuminating their autumn foliage (*colour plate 5*), gives a glory to the escarpment beech woods.

Where the woods have a greater variety of trees and include mature oak and ash, as well as beech, light more easily penetrates to ground level and so there is a richer flora. The understorey here commonly contains maple, hazel and dogwood, in addition to the evergreens mentioned above. Dog's mercury, primrose, sanicle, yellow archangel and, later in the year, the nettle-leafed bell flower are abundant. Some woods are noted for particular flowers such as lily of the valley (*19*) and angular Solomon's seal at Siccaridge and autumn crocus at Chatcombe. A hundred years ago writers referred to Chedworth and Guiting Woods as being magnets for botanists. However, the general abandonment of coppicing, which allowed the ground flora to flourish for a while, and the immediate post-war policy of clear felling, stump removal and the planting of conifers, have lessened their botanical appeal.

Many of the long, narrow strips of woodland just above the damp meadows of the valley floors are used for pheasant rearing, and during the shooting season the fields below are marked out for the shooting positions when beaters work through the woods. Tens of thousands of pheasants and many partridges are reared each year on the Cotswolds for game shooting. Other small woods have been reserved as fox coverts. These are dense woods, often with conifers and without footpath access, which give security for the fox earths. The coverts are spaced out to give goods runs for the hunt. Significantly, when the large estates

19 Lily of the valley has spread over the steep, stoney slopes in Siccaridge Wood, near Sapperton

were broken up and farmland sold off in the inter-war period, the coverts were retained by the estates to ensure good hunting in future years. If fox hunting ceases there will be no need to retain these woods and a very characteristic feature of the Cotswold landscape may disappear. Other small but more regularly-shaped woods, with trees of uniform size and type, are plantations. Sometimes the name indicates the date of the original planting such as Waterloo Larch at Temple Guiting. Plantations on the Cotswolds are normally of larch or pine, but sometimes these trees only border an interior of beech, and there are poplar plantations in the valleys.

Farmers on the Cotswolds were encouraged to grow ash trees in the hedgerows and beside field walls. These provided useful farm timber and fuel in addition to shelter for livestock. Beech was often planted beside isolated and exposed farms to give protection from prevailing winds.

But the trees in our landscape have not been grown only for their shelter, timber, or other wood products, they have also been grown for their beauty. Frequently they have been planted for ornamental purposes to enhance the appearance of country estates. Avenues of trees gave an indication of the extent of an estate as, for example, with the Broad Walk in Cirencester Park, part planted and part cleared through woodland. Sometimes lines of trees marked estate boundaries and along the roadsides across the Cotswolds trees often grow in the hollows from which stone was quarried for road building. Clumps of beech trees, or individual specimen exotic trees such as cedars, were key features of late eighteenth- and early nineteenth-century landscaping. Many of these trees are now near the end of their life and their replacement is often problematic. There may also be more than the visual landscaping significance to their group planting. At Rendcomb, for example, the clumps are in the shapes of the Hebrew letters of the name of a former landowner, F.H. Goldsmid, and at Spring Hill near Chipping Campden, and no doubt on other estates, the trees were planted in blocks corresponding to the positioning of battalions of troops in the Napoleonic wars.

From Georgian times trees were given symbolic meanings. Oak represented stability and longevity and so was often used as a backdrop to family portraits. Beech, with its spreading branches and summer shade, indicated hospitality and shelter, and elm was associated with a well-managed farming landscape. Conifers

20 The Tortworth Chestnut. Several trunks rise from the stool of this coppiced tree which is thought to be about 1,200 years old

were less favoured. They were introduced species and associated with new money, often from industry, as distinct from the inherited wealth of the landed gentry. Respect is still shown to very old trees such as the Tortworth Chestnut (20) in South Gloucestershire, thought to date from about AD 800, and the small leaf lime tree in Silkwood at Westonbirt, whose wide coppiced stool may be 2,000 years old. Both have been recently designated as heritage trees. The famous Newland Oak has now gone, but a young descendant has been planted beside the remains of the parent tree.

Gloucestershire also possesses several nationally important collections of trees introduced from other parts of the world. The National Arboretum at Westonbirt, developed by the Forestry Commission from the first plantings by Robert Holford in 1829, and the Batsford Park Arboretum dating from 1888, are the largest and noted for their spectacular autumn displays of acers (*colour plate 7*). Colesbourne Park has some rare trees besides its famous snowdrop collection and the Cyril Hart Arboretum near the Speech House and the small memorial garden in Chipping Campden, dedicated to the plant collector Ernest Wilson, have others.

On the rising ground towards the Forest at Blaisdon and Pope's Hill; around Minsterworth, Hartpury and Dymock; and on the eastern side of the Severn in the Vale of Berkeley, many farms and smallholdings had their orchards of apples, pears and plums. This was cider and perry country and, although many orchards have gone since the Second World War, some orchards remain and there are many plots with a few neglected fruit trees. The varieties, of which there were more than a hundred, were mainly local to the area and the apples were rich in tannin, rather like crab apples. The strength of the farmhouse cider was thought to vary with the soil as well as with the variety of fruit. Much cider was consumed by the farm workers and the daily allowance for each labourer at hay making and harvest time was two gallons! Casual labourers were also attracted by the quality of the farmer's cider. The hum of bees at blossom time, the smell of the piles, or tumps, of slowly rotting apples in autumn, and the winter silhouette of the orchard trees against a blue sky impressed several of the county's early twentieth-century writers including Algernon Gissing, Will Harvey and Henry Warren. The movement of cold air over the river and the slightly higher ground of the orchards reduced the risk of frost by checking early blossom and preventing cold air from stagnating. Many farms still possess the cider mills – circular stone troughs of Quartz Conglomerate from the Forest into which the apples were tipped to be crushed by a stone runner pulled round by one or more horses. Leonard Clark, writing nostalgically of his childhood at Cinderford, puts it like this:

21 A popular local variety of plum – the Blaisdon

> They are gone now, cider-house and orchards,
> and billowing tides of blossoms riding the slopes,
> with early bees raiding, and Severn, a silver eel,
> twisting to the sea on the far-away skyline.
> The magical names remain,
> those old apples of cidered Gloucestershire,
> Skyrmes Kernel, Dymock Red, and Forest Styre,
> Black Foxwhelps and Redstreak;
> such honeyed sounds,
> pure English poetry in my country ears.

Westbury Court garden has a collection of seventeenth-century varieties of fruit trees, and near the bee shelter at the back of the churchyard at Hartpury is a small collection of old varieties of pear trees, including the local variety Hartpury Green. Blaisdon plums (*21*) are still commercially grown and sold for cooking.

In recent years grants have been available to farmers to plant woods on former farmland. There has been a limited uptake, mainly on steeper slopes on the Cotswolds, and it is not yet possible to assess the visual impact they will make.

So whether planted for strategic, commercial, ecological, amenity or ornamental reasons trees are major features of our landscape and with their different sizes, forms and colours contribute significantly to its interest, variety and beauty.

4

The farming landscape – fields and farms

Most fields in Gloucestershire date from the period of Parliamentary Enclosures, roughly between 1730 and 1830, but there are many traces of earlier fields and field boundaries. The oldest are the faint markings of Celtic fields. With a slight dusting of snow and a low angle of sunlight in winter it is possible to recognise the outlines of these small, roughly rectangular fields. On sloping ground soil was loosened by primitive criss-cross ploughing and moved downhill under gravity. At the lower edges of the fields it accumulated to give small terraces, and where there has not been subsequent cultivation these terraces many still be seen. Examples can be seen on Ablington Downs just east of Winson; on the north side of the Leach valley where it is crossed by Akeman Street near Eastleach Turville; and on Barrington Downs east of Aldsworth. They differ in size and clarity from the much later medieval lynchet fields which were produced in a similar way but with larger ploughs, and on a bigger scale. Lynchets are well preserved on the hillsides near Farmcote and north of Wotton-under-Edge.

There are also thought to be traces of Roman centuriation near Brockworth. Here rectangular blocks of land may be identified from field boundaries and may correspond to land granted to pensioned-off Roman soldiers from Glevum. Also, a faint grid of old field boundaries is aligned to the walls of the Roman villa at Barnsley Park and we would expect to find others around the numerous villa sites.

22 Cotswold Sheep. These two sheep in an enclosure of hurdles were part of the last commercial flock of the breed at Aldsworth. They are long-legged animals and their wool is parted along their backs and hangs in ringlets down their noses. They are similar to the engravings of sheep on the brasses of wool merchants in Northleach Church

From Saxon times to the Enclosure period most of the farming areas of the county were characterised by very large open fields. The grazing of livestock was on common pasture, large areas of the Cotswolds were downs for sheep grazing (*22*), and crops were grown on common arable fields. The number of common arable fields in a parish varied with soil fertility. Thus, on the thin brashy soils of the Cotswolds there were normally two fields where crops and fallow alternated annually; whereas on the naturally more fertile soils of the Vale three fields were common and crops could be grown on two successive years before the fallow year restored fertility. Near the villages there were small closes and also some plots on which weed-infested crops were grown every year.

The common fields were divided into smaller units known as furlongs, each of which consisted of a numbers of strips. A strip was the basic unit of cultivation and usually represented one day's ploughing. Early ploughs only cut a single furrow and on heavy soils four pairs of oxen were required to pull the plough. As holdings were small, each farmer could provide no more than one or two oxen for the plough and therefore ploughing was a communal activity, ideal for a settlement pattern in which the farms were all located together in the village. The plough had a fixed mould board which meant that the soil could be turned

23 Ridge and furrow near Alderton. Furlong boundaries were where the direction of the ridges changes. Notice the curves of the ridges which indicate ploughing by oxen. Where a hedge marks the line where the ridge and furrow changes direction it may pre-date Enclosure

over in one direction only. The maximum length of the strips corresponded to the distance oxen could pull the plough before needing a rest, and so on the heavy clay soils strips were shorter than on lighter soils and were also wider because more short furrows could be turned in a day. Ploughing began at the centre of the end of a strip and returned from the centre at the other end, so the soil from the first two furrows was heaped together. Ploughing then continued up and down opposite sides. Centuries of ploughing in this way led to the strips becoming ridged. The characteristic ridge and furrow pattern of the north of the Vale was produced in this way (*23*). Even today the difference in height between the top of the ridge and the bottom of the furrow can be as much as 3-4ft, but eighteenth-century writers say that sometimes the ridges were so high that plough teams were hidden from each other as they worked in different parts of the same field. To prevent the oxen trampling over the strips of the adjacent furlong at the end of the furrow, the ploughs were gradually turned before the end of the strip was reached and the plough teams were then reversed on the headland. This gave the typical reverse S-shape to the strip. After enclosure this heavy clay land was usually devoted to pasture and in some places has never been ploughed since. The ridge and furrow pattern has been fossilised in the landscape.

From the changes of direction of the corrugations in the fields the outlines of the former furlongs can also be traced. The soil in the hollows is colder and wetter than that of the raised areas and often the grassland plant communities reflect this. In early summer the fields are striped with bands of buttercups in flower on the ridges. Corn yields were always higher on the ridges than in the furrows. Undoubtedly the ridge and furrow system improves the drainage of the ridges but at the expense of the furrows.

A communal system of farming such as this meant that on one day the plough was worked on one man's land and on subsequent days on the land of other landholders. As each holding consisted of a number of strips of land, they were scattered widely over the common fields. It was an equitable system in that each farmer had a share in the varied soils of the parish and also a fair share of travel distance to his land, some strips being close to the farmyard, others being further away. Not all the arable land of every parish was managed in this way, however, and from the fourteenth century blocks of land were enclosed for independent management. These were normally away from the village.

By the eighteenth century the numerous disadvantages of the common field system of farming were clearly apparent – at least to the landowners. Much time and effort was involved in reaching the widely scattered strips of the fragmented holdings, and this was an important issue especially when improving the land by manuring was considered. Applications of manure were easily given to nearby strips but not to the more remote ones, and much cultivable land was wasted because access routes were required for each strip. Farming decisions about what crops were to be grown and what grazing arrangements were to be adopted were communal, and so individual farmer initiative was stifled. Where livestock were concerned they grazed together on common land and it was therefore difficult to control the spread of disease, or to regulate breeding. And probably of greatest importance to the landowners was the fact that the rent from common land was about half that from enclosed land. So a procedure for reorganising the layout of the farms was set in motion.

The Act announcing the 1732 Enclosure Award for Upper and Lower Slaughter contains a typical eighteenth-century argument for enclosure. It states that

whereas the several arable lands and grounds of the respective freeholders and land owners lie intermixed and dispersed in small parcels in and over the said common fields of Lower Slaughter and Upper Slaughter respectively, and are most of them inconveniently situated with respect to their several houses in the said parishes, and by reason thereof a sufficient quantity of soil, dung and compost cannot, without great expense, be conveyed to manure the same, whereby, and for want of inclosed grounds to keep a stock of cattle, the said common fields are greatly impoverished, and as some of the common fields and common grounds in both the said parishes lie contiguous to and unseparated from each other, and are inter-commoned and depastured with the cattle belonging to both the said parishes promiscuously, frequent trespass and disputes arise between the several proprietors, and so long as the said common fields and common grounds lie open, undivided and uninclosed, they produce little profit to the respective owners thereof, and are in a great measure rendered incapable of improvement.

To manure all the strips of the large Manor Farm at Lower Slaughter with dung carried by cart, or 'dung pot', from the farmyard and spread at the rate of ten loads per acre would have involved travelling more than 3,200 miles!

Once agreement to enclose the land had been reached between the landowners, or the majority of them, a bill was presented to Parliament through the county MP. Following the Act, commissioners were appointed to oversee the process. The land was surveyed and valued and all the claims to it were considered. This was often a complex process because land was not only the ground on which crops could be grown and livestock reared, it was also a 'repository of rights' entitling the holder to various privileges in the manor. A number of the superb large scale maps showing the landholdings of all the farmers of the parish survive. Then the land was reallocated in more compact units as equitably as possible, either close to the existing farm buildings of the landholder, or where new buildings could be conveniently erected. There has been some debate as to the fairness of the land redistribution but the evidence suggests that the commissioners acted impartially – as they promised to do.

After the land for each holding had been marked out, the planting of hedges and the construction of dry stone walls around the farm boundary began, and subsequently the internal field boundaries were also formed. Because a seven-year crop rotation system was popular on the Cotswolds at the time, many farms here were divided into seven fields in addition to the home field close to the farmyard. This field was kept as pasture, partly to facilitate access to the other fields, and partly for assembling dairy cattle at milking time.

Thus the appearance of the countryside was completely changed in a very short period of time. New roads were laid out and new farmhouses, or isolated barns, were built if the landholding was allocated at a distance from the original farm in the village. At the same time tithes were commuted, and the tithe holder was given an equivalent amount of land. This was usually at the edge of the parish, so here large new farms were formed. Only in exceptional circumstances can such a major change to landholding take place. It requires both a powerful change factor and a low resistance to change. These conditions occurred at different times in different parishes but by the early nineteenth century the change was more or less complete.

The enclosure awards on the Cotswolds specified the dimensions of the dry stone walls. They were to be 4ft 8in high, 2ft 4in wide at the base and 1ft 6in wide at the top and cost 5s (25p) a perch (c.5m). As frost weathering can cause rapid deterioration of these walls, they were constructed to have good drainage by a rubble infill and outward sloping stones. Nearly all the Cotswold field boundary walls date from the time of the Parliamentary Enclosures. When hedges were used as farm and field boundaries, which was normal in the Vale and in the north-west of the county, they were planted between two parallel fences of posts and rails on the heaped-up soil beside a newly dug ditch. The species of shrub were chosen to give stock-proof hedges and were normally hawthorn and blackthorn. After the shrubs had become established, at seven years, the hedges were 'plashed' and the fences removed. It is in this manner that most of our hedges have been formed. Older hedges than these are distinguished by having a greater variety of shrubs growing in them, sometimes because they were originally formed from woodland, sometimes because they have been repaired many times with other available shrubs, and mainly because they have been colonised by other species over the years. Hooper's law that the age of a hedge can be estimated by the number of woody species in a 30m stretch (where the age in years is 110, multiplied by the number of species, plus 30) does not quite fit Gloucestershire hedges. However, the number of species does enable us to distinguish between a Saxon parish boundary hedge, a Tudor enclosure and an eighteenth-century Parliamentary Enclosure hedge (*colour plate 8*). Individual species may also be used to indicate the age of a hedge. Hedges containing hazel and spindle are probably pre-1500 and field maple also suggests an older hedge. Elder spreads quickly so cannot be used in dating.

Recently the general condition of field boundaries has deteriorated. This is because of the high labour costs of good quality maintenance. Another factor is the decline in mixed farming; when fields were used both for arable crops and for livestock all boundaries had to be stock-proof. The relative cheapness of wire netting has reduced the need for such labour intensive skilled work. Larger fields enable farm machinery to be worked more efficiently and hedgerows take nutrients from the soil, shade areas of cropland and harbour pests. So there are good reasons for removing or reducing hedges and walls. On the other hand hedges are important nesting habitats for birds, they provide shelter and runways for small mammals and they form a backdrop for the many hedgerow flowers. Ancient hedges in particular have high ecological and conservation value. It is now illegal to remove an old hedge and some DEFRA (Dept. for Environment, Food and Rural Affairs) grants are designed to protect hedges in the future. Both walls and hedges contribute to the scenic quality of our landscapes.

The newly laid-out farms gave their owners, or tenants, the opportunity to farm independently and to experiment with new crops and animal breeding.

The traditional practice of growing wheat, barley and beans gave way to more complex arrangements such as the seven year rotation followed on the Cotswolds. This rotation was of turnips, barley, grass (for hay), grass (for grazing), wheat, oats/peas/vetch and sainfoin. Sheep feeding on turnips and grass and cattle feeding on grass, hay and sainfoin would provide manure; peas, vetch and sainfoin are nitrogen fixing crops; and cultivation of the fields at different times of the year for the various crops checked the spread of weeds and pests. In this way all farmland was productive and the practice was sustainable. Specialist breeds of livestock were now kept. Hampshire Downs crossed with Oxford Downs sheep became popular on the Cotswolds and Gloucester cattle (*24*), which provided milk for the original Double Gloucester cheese, predominated in the Vale. Some farmers became noted for their skill in breeding quality livestock. Herds of Suffolk Dun, Red Poll and Devon as well as Shorthorn and Longhorn were kept. And the landscape became much more varied and colourful. The bright pink of sainfoin was often reported by travellers.

There was also greater prosperity in farming and with such varied activity farm labourers were fully occupied throughout the year. But there were social costs to

24 The Gloucester breed of cow. The dark brown body and white stripe along its backbone and white tail are distinguishing features of this breed which produced milk for the Double Gloucester cheese. The cheese was called Double Gloucester because full cream milk from both morning and evening milkings was used. For Single Gloucester the evening milk was first skimmed so that the cream could be used for butter making

25 Open field at Dixton Manor. This well known painting shows hay making in the eighteenth century. Teams of workers scythe the grass and rake the hay to the music of a fiddler or a hurdy-gurdy. It reminds us that many people were involved in work on the land in those days in contrast to the lonely work of a tractor driver today. *Cheltenham Museum*

Parliamentary Enclosure. The dispersal of some farmers from the villages to new outlying farms disrupted village life. The loss of common land meant that landless labourers had no grazing for their livestock, or sources of fuel in the patches of furze that were once abundant, and the rhythmic scything or raking of grass and wheat by teams of workers to the sounds of the hurdy-gurdy or fiddle as shown in the painting of Dixton Manor (*25*) became a distant memory.

Water meadows were formed beside the rivers. Frequently a herringbone pattern of channels was dug on these meadows to allow water to flood the land in the winter. Sluice gates controlled the flow. The water brought silt, which maintained fertility, and kept the soil warmer than otherwise, which enabled rapid growth of grass once the land had been drained in early spring. Heavy crops of hay were produced once the grazing of the 'early bite' had ceased. Water meadows were common along the Coln (*26*) and the Windrush. At Naunton they were known as the 'Swillies', and at Sherborne the National Trust has recently restored them to working condition. Along the Severn in winter, river water frequently floods the Hams with the same effect, but these floods are not so readily controlled by man.

26 A landscape of Parliamentary Enclosure at Coln Rogers. The River Coln is bordered by a small wood and the lower part of the sheep pasture shows the faint channels of a water meadow

Until recently most farms were rented from the principal landowners and it was therefore relatively easy for the size of farm units to be changed. This was usually to fewer and larger units. Once owner occupancy became normal, changes to farm sizes have become more difficult.

Towards the end of the nineteenth century farm prosperity in general began to decline. The governments of the day gave priority to the provision of cheap food for the growing urban and industrial populations. A vast empire where large-scale agricultural production at low cost was possible, cheap shipping with a navy to protect the merchant ships, and later the invention of refrigeration, meant that imported food could be brought into the country more cheaply than our farmers could produce. In order to survive they had to make changes to their output. Milk, fruit and vegetables were perishable and less suitable for long distance transport, so these became the new emphases. Much former arable land was converted to pasture, and market gardening spread into areas having suitable soils and good access to the urban markets. The Vale specialised in dairying and the area around Newent focused on fruit and vegetables. Farming on the Cotswolds was particularly depressed. There were, however, checks on this open market policy. The risk of a wartime shipping blockade, which would have prevented the import of overseas food, meant that for national security some arable farming was essential. Not all areas of Britain were suitable for pastoral farming and market gardening, and the rural populations in those areas needed support. Therefore, a complex and frequently changing system of artificial farm support began and farmers have responded in various ways to this system.

The entry of Britain into the Common Market and in particular the implementation of the 1962 Common Agricultural Policy, brought prosperity back to many Cotswold farmers because the new emphasis was upon cereals – and the Cotswolds are well suited to modern cereal production. In addition to cereals, CAP encouraged an expansion of other arable crops such as oil seed rape and linseed, which have been grown on a small scale in Gloucestershire since the sixteenth and seventeenth centuries respectively. These, too, grow well here and from this time the Cotswolds began to feel the full impact of intensive agriculture. The costs of upgrading farm dairies after the Second World War had reduced the number of small farms producing milk and now the large specialist dairy farms also prospered. The Friesian became the most popular dairy breed because of its high milk yields and the beef rearing potential of its surplus calves, particularly if they were cross bred with a Hereford bull. Continental beef breeds such as Charollais were introduced on some specialist beef farms.

By the 1980s concerns were being raised about the costs incurred by the over-production of cereals and milk and about the environmental effects of intensive farming. Enlargement of fields to facilitate the working of large harvesting machines involves the removal of hedges and walls; the continuous use of chemical fertilisers on arable land has a long-term effect of weakening soil structures and eliminates the need for livestock as a source of manure; the chemical sprays used to kill pests and weeds and to check diseases not only have ecological consequences for wild flowers, insects and birds but also mean that crop rotation is no longer necessary and extensive monoculture can result. Heavy applications of nitrate fertilisers, and especially the spreading of slurry to increase the rate of grass growth on dairy farms, leads to leaching and the eutrophication of water courses unless carefully monitored. People became aware that scenically the countryside was becoming less diverse, large modern farm buildings were more intrusive, wildlife was declining and the economics of farm subsidies were being questioned.

Attempts were then made to change CAP so as to curb over-production and to protect the environment. Quotas were introduced to limit milk production, prices for cereals were allowed to fall and grants were made available to encourage environmentally friendly farming. The impact of Stewardship Schemes and of grants in Environmentally Sensitive Areas has been mixed. Generally the larger farms, with adequate capital reserves and in areas where the land is suitable for intensive farming, have continued in this way, though with much smaller profits. And arable fields treated as set-aside, reminiscent of the 'tumbled down land' at the end of the nineteenth century, indicate that farming today is not flourishing. The uptake of conservation grants on the less productive land such as the Cotswold edge and on the margins of the Forest has been more common. Farmers have been encouraged to diversify and as they have searched for new markets, lupins, sage, evening primrose, lavender and borage (*colour plate 9*) have been grown successfully on a small scale, bringing new colours to the landscape. On the shooting estates, strips of maize and sunflowers border some fields and equestrian centres have mushroomed. But it remains to be seen how the latest policy for environmentally friendly farming affects the landscape. Support for farmers is now based on a tiered system of payments depending on the range of conservation measures adopted. Maintenance of hedgerows, planting woodland trees, preserving old pastures (*colour plate 10*), restoring traditional farm buildings and creating ponds are some of the favoured measures, and organic farming is encouraged. The spread of scrub and coarse vegetation on the commons is being checked by the grazing of Belted Galloway and Welsh Black cattle, which can over-winter on the hills and can utilise the poor pasture. Sheep are slowly returning to the Forest from which they were eliminated by the livestock cull resulting from foot and mouth disease. But there are still problems, and the spread of plastic tunnelling for horticulture is a highly visible one. How far population growth, climatic change, rising costs of oil and investment in biomass fuel crops will affect farming in general is also unknown.

To maintain the perceived attractiveness of the rural landscape farming has to be profitable everywhere. However, it is likely that constraint is necessary for some farming practices. Negative externality in which costs of production are offloaded to others is not confined to industry, it has become a feature of some intensive agriculture as well.

5

Houses – great and small

With an almost continuous modern building programme, particularly in the Severn Valley, houses have become increasingly conspicuous elements in the landscape. The views west from Crickley Hill over Gloucester, or from Cleeve Hill over Bishop's Cleeve and Cheltenham, clearly demonstrate this.

Most modern housing is standardised and uses designs and materials that are available throughout the country, with little regard to local conditions. But before the advent of canals and railways and later of lorry transport, which provided a sequence of cheap ways to carry bulky building materials, houses were built from local resources. At a distance of 12 miles from the quarry, the cost of transporting stone by road using horse-drawn wagons exceeded the cost of the stone itself. So with the exception of the large country houses and a few riverside properties, the materials for house building had to come from the immediate neighbourhood, and in most cases from the same parish. For the Cotwolds this local material was oolitic limestone, for the Severn Vale it was timber and brick, and for the Forest of Dean and surrounding areas, sandstone. As we shall see, the type of building material inevitably affects the form and plan of the house, and it therefore contributes greatly to the variations in appearance of houses across the county. Frequently early houses had economic functions as well as being dwelling places, and these uses together with the contrasting wealth of their owners or occupants, which also varied from one area to another, give added emphasis to the variations. When we reach the late nineteenth century, however, there is a significant change in house construction. This is particularly noticeable in rural areas, where imported materials and the uniformity of design coincided with decline in agricultural employment.

In the Cotswolds the majority of parishes had their own quarries, from which building stone was obtained. Here stone began to replace timber framing for house construction in the fifteenth century. The stone varies in quality. Where freestone such as Taynton stone was available, walls were built entirely of large blocks. Elsewhere walls were generally of rubble with dressed stone for the corners or quoins, and for key structural components. When oolitic limestone has been freshly quarried it may be chiselled into delicate forms, and the stone then hardens on exposure to the weather. This enables door frames and window frames to be of stone rather than of wood, and stone mullion and transomed windows are typical of the area. A protective and decorative course of stonework projecting out above the doors and windows, like 'square eyebrows' and known as drip moulds or labels is also common (27), although in parishes where the stone is weaker these are less likely. In the humbler cottages the lintels are often of oak. At the end of the sixteenth century it was discovered that some limestone

27 A cottage by the green at Guiting Power. Notice the pronounced drip mould or label

28 A cottage at Temple Guiting with both dormer and gable windows and oak lintels

could be split into thin slates for roofing, and so Stonesfield slates began to replace thatch. Both wet thatch and Cotswold slates are heavy, so to prevent the weight of these heavy roofs from pushing the walls outwards, the pitch of the roof had to be steep, often at about 55 degrees. This has two consequences. First, there is a high roof space to be used and, secondly, the houses are narrower from front to back than they would be with a pitch gentler than that common on the Cotswolds. The roof space was used for bedrooms, lit by dormer or gable windows, and the narrow plan meant that the through rooms could be lit by windows front and back (*28*). To increase the size of the house the simple linear plan could be elaborated into an L-shape, or a U-shape around a central courtyard. Roof slates vary in size, with the largest laid at the eaves and the smallest at the ridge. Each of the 24 sizes of slate has its own name. The slates were fixed to the roof laths by oak pegs and bedded on moss. Many of the older roofs sag; this is partly due to the bending of the roof timbers, but it also ensures that the slates fit tightly together and so prevents the wind from lifting them. The roofs of manor houses and other wealthier properties are usually embellished with carved finials on the gable ends.

The harmonious relationship of Cotswold buildings, when viewed together, results from the use of the same building materials and building methods for houses of all social levels, in cottages and farmhouses, in rectories and manors.

29 Cromwell House, Naunton. This rubble and part rough cast house is probably the oldest in the village, dating from about 1600

Barns, sheds, mills and dovecotes are also in the same style, a style which has continued through the centuries (29).

When cheap bricks, corrugated iron and Welsh slates were introduced as building materials, particularly around the railway stations, objections were soon raised. Followers of the Arts and Crafts movement were outspoken critics and encouraged new building in the vernacular style. Around Chipping Campden, C.R. Ashbee and F.L. Griggs were influential in preserving the Cotswold style; near Stow, Guy Dawber was responsible for several new houses that were in keeping with the old; and around Sapperton, Ernest Barnsley and later Norman Jewson have left their mark on new and restored houses. Sympathetic restoration in the early twentieth century of the houses in Stanton by the architect Philip Stott, who bought the estate in 1906, accounts for the showpiece appearance of this village. The influence of these architects on subsequent tastes in Cotswold building has been great.

Many old Cotswold manor houses date from the seventeenth century when there was a major rebuilding programme. Some of these, such as the manors at Bibury, Buckland and Lower Slaughter, have become hotels and a few others such as Owlpen (30) and Snowshill are regularly open to the public. Another

1 A view from Shurdington Hill

2 Puzzle Wood. An ancient iron mining area near Coleford. Miners followed the seams of haematite and cut these deep trenches in doing so

3 Soil erosion in a field at Compton Abdale, December 1994. Heavy rain before the autumn sown crop had covered the soil-produced gulleys and spread the fine eroded material in a fan at the lower side of the field

4 A typical spread of pebbles on the Woolridge terrace. Notice the large pebble that has been split by severe frost

5 An autumn scene in Russells Inclosure, Forest of Dean. These mature trees were planted in about 1812

6 Beech woods at Cranham. These trees are planted close together to produce tall straight trunks suitable for making veneers

7 The brilliant colouring of the acers in Batsford Arboretum attract many visitors

8 A Cotswold hedge. The number of different shrubs in a hedge is often an indicator of its age. New foliage in the spring and the autumn colouring of the leaves, as here, make it easier to identify the shrubs. Enclosure hedges are predominantly composed of hawthorn and blackthorn and these shrubs are most conspicuous when in blossom

9 A colourful field of borage. Borage is one of the new crops farmers have grown as they seek to diversify. It is used in alternative medicine. As the mauve flowers opened in this field at Coberley so too did the scarlet poppies, making a spectacular and unplanned display

10 Flowers of an old meadow. Meadows such as this are rare today, and a farmer can receive grants to maintain it in this condition. Most grassland has been reseeded to grow more nutritious livestock food and the variety of plants has been diminished thereby

11 Abbey Cottages, Tewkesbury. These fifteenth-century terraced cottages had shops at ground floor level

12 Apart from its fifteenth-century tower the church at Elkstone is Norman with many finely carved features. Its south doorway, corbel-table, chancel arch and stone vaulted roof have delightful figures. Notice the small east window

13 Selsley church stands high above the Stroud valley. It was built in 1860-2 by G.F. Bodley and is notable for its stained glass windows by William Morris. The west window celebrating the creation is especially colourful

14 A view of Westbury Court Garden from the pavilion. Notice the characteristic topiary which is reflected in the canal water

15 The Chapel Garden, Sudeley Castle. The stonework of the castle forms the backdrop to many colourful modern plantings, in this case to a design by the late Rosemary Verey

16 Imperial Gardens, Cheltenham. These award-winning gardens have been laid out on the site of the former Winter Gardens, a glass building constructed in 1879 on land that was formerly Hodges Nursery Grounds

17 Gallops for the racing stables at Jackdaws Castle near Ford. This area of the Cotswolds is noted for training racehorses and although the surfaces of the gallops here are synthetic the naturally well-drained, springy turf is ideal for the purpose

18 A summer afternoon at Bourton-on-the-Water. Most of the commercial activity here is directed towards tourists. It is a very successful tourist 'honeypot' and is advertised as the 'Venice of the Cotswolds'. Some may prefer to visit in winter when its finer qualities may be appreciated more easily

19 Gloucester docks showing some of the early nineteenth-century warehouses and the cathedral tower in the background

20 The urban sprawl of Cheltenham as seen from Leckhampton Hill. Some of the modern peripheral developments may be seen including the newly built GCHQ just to the right of centre in the middle distance. There is constant pressure to build on greenfield sites

21 Drying tower for wool at Woodchester. This eighteenth-century building has had a variety of uses and has now been converted into a house

22 A late eighteenth-century painting of part of Stroud showing the famous scarlet cloth being dyed at Wallbridge and cloth of various colours drying on racks in the fields above. Notice the Severn trow bringing coal along the Stroudwater canal. *Stroud Museum*

23 Egypt Mill, Nailsworth. The same arrangement of seventeenth-century clothier's house and early eighteenth-century rebuilt mill has been repeated in many cases. Here the modern use is as a restaurant

24 Darkhill Iron Works near Coleford, one of the most important historical industrial sites in the world

25 Keble's Bridge which connects Eastleach Martin with Eastleach Turville. It is much older than the time when John Keble was curate at the two churches here. The daffodils lining the river banks are spectacular in the spring

30 Owlpen Manor. The building of this fine manor house began in the fifteenth century and there have been many subsequent alterations. It was restored from semi-dereliction by Norman Jewson in the 1920s. Its early eighteenth-century garden is discussed in chapter 7

rebuilding programme occurred in the nineteenth century with Cowley, Rendcomb and Sherborne. The Italianate style used in some of these is less in keeping with their Cotswold surroundings. Rodmarton Manor was the last to be built on traditional lines and is significant not only for the architectural work of Ernest Barnsley but also for its collection of contemporary furniture from the Sapperton workshop. The unfinished Woodchester Mansion, deep in its secluded, wooded valley and built in the 1860s, reveals the potential of oolitic limestone for house construction. For in addition to the basic structure of the building, stone is used for stairs, drainpipes and even a bath.

Where space allowed, the great houses of the Cotswolds were sited to overlook their grounds and orientated so that the principal rooms faced north or east. Until the late eighteenth century it was considered injurious to face the sun, particularly with its glare on the evening dinner table.

Today, planning regulations require new buildings to be in keeping with their neighbours. Synthetic stone for walls and roofs generally replicates the colour and appearance of oolitic limestone and is easier and less costly to use than quarried stone, but it is still more expensive than bricks and concrete tiles, and may not weather in the same way as the traditional stone. As a consequence new houses on the Cotswolds are generally more expensive than those elsewhere in the county, with the result that many younger local people are priced out of the market. Disused barns and other old farm buildings have been converted to homes and acquired by retired people and commuting executives, and some small cottages have become second homes. Thus housing availability and costs have had a major effect on the social make up and population turnover of Cotswold villages. The houses themselves are in a better state of repair than they have ever been, but are no longer occupied by the type of people for whom they were originally built. Polished oak doors, discrete double glazing, wrought iron lamps, burglar alarms, gravel drives and landscape-designed gardens have largely replaced peeling paintwork, net curtains and front gardens devoted to vegetable plots and old cars. Many cottages have been extended to provide more space than eighteenth- and nineteenth-century families were used to, and a recent development has been the addition of conservatories.

Estate villages frequently possess cottages of similar designs, as for example at Sherborne, and as we note later, paint work of the same colour is typical of these settlements. Also particular styles of cottage may occur frequently in some places. For example, in Bibury the cross-passage cottage is common and may be identified by the front door being just to one side of a line drawn vertically through the central chimney (47).

Scarp foot villages also had quarries in the Inferior Oolite at the top of the slope and many houses, and particularly the more important ones such as the manor houses, are built in the Cotswold style. But as we move away from the hills different materials have been introduced and soon begin to dominate. Bricks made from Lias Clay form the walls and clay tiles, the roofs. The earliest bricks were handmade, thin and variable in size and may be seen in late seventeenth- and eighteenth-century properties. The bonding styles vary and some brickwork is very elaborate. Near the Severn the clay used for bricks sometimes contained salts and this gives mottled colouring and frequent cracks in the bricks, so common around Frampton (31). Major brickworks were later established at Tuffley and Stonehouse. Close to the Gloucester–Sharpness Canal bricks of different colours were brought in by boat and this explains the decorative designs in the houses at Saul. Imported pantiles are also to be found on the roofs of eighteenth-century houses in this area. A special feature of the farmhouses in the Berkeley area, where dairying was so important, is the occurrence of louvres in the attics. Double Gloucester cheeses were stored in these attics. In the cider areas cider barns sometimes housed the mill and press, as at Taynton House. Here high quality, late seventeenth- or early eighteenth-century brick farm buildings with stone roofs enclose the farmyard, with the house occupying the south side of this secluded property.

31 An interesting pair of cottages at Frampton. Bricks have been made on the Frampton Court estate and are frequently mottled from salts in the clay

Half-timbered houses are also common in the Vale. Oak was used for the framework, and builders selected the timber on the trees for size and shape, rather than sawing construction timber from felled trees. The wood was used green and this led to subsequent warping. Bricks were normally used to fill in between the timber framework, but wattle and daub can also be found. It is said that along the drove roads – the tracks that cattle drovers followed as they crossed the county going from Wales towards Smithfield market – the abundance of cattle hair strengthened the plaster. Oak was not the only timber to be used. Elm from hedgerow timber was occasionally used and on the wet, poorly drained meadows by the Severn another important tree, the Black Poplar, was once abundant. These have large, rough, curved branches which were cut to provide the frame for cruck houses. The exposed end timbers of cruck houses may be seen at Apperley, Didbrook, Dymock and Sandhurst.

The Great House at Hasfield (*32*) has a striking combination of materials, for its south front is built partly of Lias Limestone, part is half-timbered and part brick.

Many half-timbered houses in towns had jetties. Usually their structural timbers and studding are left exposed but when fashions changed some have been plastered over. Jetties protected the walls and doorways below. They also

32 The Great House, Hasfield, showing the full range of building materials used in the Vale

increased the floor space of upper floors, but their main use was probably to give a cantilever effect to balance the heavy oak furniture of the time and so prevent the floors from sagging. Tewkesbury is the principal place to see these and many have survived in its three main streets (*colour plate 11*).

Early paintings show Cheltenham to have been a small, red brick, settlement of one street. With the Regency exploitation of spa waters the associated new housing used Cotswold stone, brought by plateway from the Leckhampton quarries, and roofs were of Welsh slate imported via Gloucester. However, once the speculation bubble had burst, brick was again used but this time masked by an ashlar facing, or stucco painted to look like stone in order to keep up appearances. Inspection of the rear of the properties usually discloses their make up. The Promenade, Cheltenham's principal street, was once lined on both sides with houses: villas on the east side and a mixture of villas and terraces on the west. One has to view the buildings from the other side of the street in order to appreciate this because the extended shop frontages on the east side mask what lies behind. Where the building of terraced housing in towns was on a small scale, it was common for each house to be built separately and the money obtained from the sale of one house was used to pay for the construction of the next. The

33 Brick terraced houses in Tewkesbury. The vertical mortar joints between the houses are often hidden by the drainpipes

vertical mortar joints between the houses are sometimes hidden behind drain pipes as in Mill Street, Tewkesbury (*33*).

Occasionally Lias Limestone is found in the older Vale buildings, though more usually in churches and barns. At Ashleworth, in addition to the tithe barn and church, the fifteenth-century Ashleworth Court is also of Lias Limestone (*34*) and so are the footings of some of the brick buildings. The stone does not weather as well as oolitic limestone and may require lime rendering. Around Newent 'Gorsley stone' was popular and to the west of the Forest some farms and old farm buildings used Quartz Conglomerate. Church Farm at Staunton is an example of the latter (*35*).

Within the crown land of the Forest of Dean there are few old houses. Squatters properties of turf-roofed, single storey, stone hovels were periodically destroyed and the population moved away. Houses that were legally erected were of stone, usually of Pennant Sandstone and Old Red Sandstone, as in the case of the Speech House. Terraced housing for miners and iron workers mostly came after the arrival of plateways and railways, and as well as local stone used cheap imported bricks and slate. There were a few brickworks in the Forest, but these were mainly producing fire bricks and materials for industrial buildings. Ballast

34 Ashleworth Court. The church, tithe barn and house are all built of Lias Limestone

35 Church Farm, Staunton. The central part of the house is built of local Quartz Conglomerate

from Severn shipping brought copper slag from Bristol to Newnham, and this too was used in a few buildings here.

After the arrival of the railways, standardised designs and materials meant that the majority of houses after this time show little differentiation from one part of the county to another, apart from the planning constraints associated with the Cotswolds. Even here recent buildings at Andoversford have used red bricks, and at Guiting Power and Northleach dark grey slates imported from Spain roof new properties.

There are also a few distinguished modern houses in the county. The well-known architect Quinlan Terry designed the solid looking Court Farm at Bibury, and at the Lower Mill Estate at Somerford Keynes some ultra-modern second homes are being built among the lakes of the Cotswold Water Park.

Generally the life expectancy of a worker's cottage was about 100 years unless it had been renovated, so in most settlements a succession of houses was built on the same plot of ground. Today, with modern building techniques and the high cost of property, renovation is more likely than demolition and rebuilding, and the latter only occurs when the grounds of an older house are used for a number of modern properties. The social trend for more and more houses for single occupancy increases the demand for smaller homes.

In this chapter we have considered the view of the house from outside, noting some of the visual differences of houses of different dates and in different parts of the county, but for their occupants the house is home. It is only the shell in which life takes place, and the inside is much more important than the outside shell. Naturally the variations of the interiors far exceed those of the exteriors.

6

Churches in the landscape

Church buildings are very conspicuous features in our landscape. Despite the fact that in towns and cities they may be overtopped by modern structures, they are usually the largest and oldest buildings in rural areas. In their fabric they not only convey information about their age and the conditions in which they were first built but also some of the social and economic changes that have occurred since then (*36*). Generally, when the worshipping population grew churches were expanded and when it declined maintenance became a problem and some churches were abandoned. With later redundant nonconformist chapels, alternative uses were sometimes found but with the parish church this was less likely. Similarly, increased wealth often led to complete rebuilding of churches and to the replacing of features that have survived intact in less prosperous areas.

Churches of different dates have different architectural features. These may follow the fashions of the time, the particular craftsmanship skills of the builders, the liturgical emphasis, or the whim of the principal benefactor. Gloucestershire is especially important for its Norman churches and for those rebuilt in the late fifteenth century with gifts from wealthy wool merchants. However, in this chapter we will look at the main characteristics of the churches at each significant period of building.

Christianity came to Gloucestershire in the Roman period. The word square, now in the Corinium Museum in Cirencester, and the chi–rho engraving on the

36 Interior of St Mary's Church, Bibury, a church in which the fabric shows many stages of development. The stonework that has been pierced by the chancel arch is Saxon. The pillars between the north aisle and the chancel are parts of the former north wall of the church. The large chancel indicates the importance of the church

stones which formerly surrounded the octagonal pool at the Chedworth Roman villa are small pieces of incidental evidence. From mid-Saxon times documents exist for land grants to various churches and monasteries, but we have to wait until the late Saxon period before we have surviving architectural remains. This is probably because the original churches were wooden, and more durable stone only became widely used after about 1050. Indicators of Saxon churches are arches cut from a single stone, tiny round-headed windows, large through stones at the corners known as 'longs and shorts', stepped footings, herringbone masonry and various decorative devices. In the Coln valley, Bibury church has a Saxon window and decorative pilaster strips of interlacing circles and pellets, and Coln Rogers has megalithic 'longs and shorts'; in the Duntisbourne valley Daglingworth has impressive Saxon sculptures and Duntisbourne Rous 'longs and shorts'; and Somerford Keynes has an arch over the north doorway cut from a single stone. However, the greatest Saxon treasure is at Deerhurst (*37*). Here, close to the Severn, but above flood levels, is a classic Saxon church. Its architectural history is complex but its tall, long nave, herringbone masonry, double triangular headed window high up on the interior west wall, and the angel sculpture on

37 The famous Saxon church at Deerhurst. It is first recorded in 804 but parts of the building date from the seventh century and some footings from the fourth century

the outside of the east wall are diagnostic. The poet Ivor Gurney once compared its form to that of 'a boy walking'. A short distance away is the simple Odda's chapel, precisely dated from a stone inscription of 1056. Before most parish churches had been established, strategically placed minsters were the bases from which priests travelled to preaching crosses. St Mary's, at Deerhurst, was one of the 20 or so minsters that served the county in Saxon times. The clustering of these Saxon relics reflects better conditions for survival rather than the original distribution pattern of churches, for with the astonishing building programme after the Norman Conquest most churches were rebuilt and earlier architectural features eradicated.

There are more than 100 Norman churches in the county. Gloucester Cathedral and Tewkesbury Abbey are the most important of these, but the Norman churches of the Cotswolds are also of national significance. The building programme in the late eleventh and twelfth centuries, when lords of manors rebuilt with stone the earlier wooden churches, or built new churches beside their manor houses, must have contributed to a major change in the landscape. The association of church and manor house, to which rectories were added centuries later, began at this time. Where the manors were held by monasteries, skilled masons were available to leave their marks on parish churches and this perhaps explains why clusters of churches have similar decorative features. The humour of the beakheads above the doorways at Elkstone and Siddington and the tree of life motif of the tympana at Dymock and Kempley and other churches are examples. The simplest form of building was of two cells forming the nave and the chancel with north and south doors to the nave. Some churches had no east window, others a very small one. As the buildings were elaborated over time central towers were added as the stone vaulted roofs indicate, arcades and narrow aisles were built and piers became more ornate. The chevron moulding of arches is widespread. Two of the finest examples of Norman churches with some later features are Elkstone on the Cotswolds (*colour plate 12*) and Bishop's Cleeve in the Vale. But the massive round pillars, 2m in diameter, of Gloucester Cathedral and Tewkesbury Abbey seem to symbolise the power, organising ability and stability of the Church in these post-Conquest years. The landscape of the county was transformed by these solid stone structures rising in almost every parish. Not only was there great architectural skill evident at the time but also fine decorative skill. One beautifully carved Norman font in Southrop church was discovered blocking a doorway, an unusual history comparable to the indignity suffered by the Saxon font at Deerhurst which had been used as a farm wash tub!

Both Gloucester Cathedral and Tewkesbury Abbey were monastic churches of the Benedictine order, located in towns and with extensive monastic buildings attached to them. There were monasteries of other orders too. In Cirencester there was a great Augustinian Abbey located beside the present parish church. In Gloucester, Llanthony Priory and St Oswald's Priory were both Augustinian and there were religious houses here of Greyfriars, Blackfriars and Whitefriars. Remains of all except the last are still to be seen. Away from the towns Cistercians sought remote sites, fruitful, wooded and with springs. A local writer in the time of Henry II says 'They choose a place fit for habitation, fertile, good for fruit, suitable for grain, buried in woods, abounding in springs, a horn of plenty, a place apart from the haunts of men.' There were two small abbeys at Kingswood and Flaxley (*38*) with such sites and then the richly endowed abbey at Hailes. Hailes was a centre of pilgrimage to see the relic of Christ's blood and the tracks along which pilgrims travelled can be identified today. Pilgrims required accommodation and several inns originated for this purpose, including the New Inn in Gloucester and the former George Hotel in Winchcombe. The abbeys had land on the Cotswolds where large flocks of sheep were kept. Wool was an important source of income for them, and in the case of the Cistercians the monks themselves managed the flocks, using granges as their outlying bases.

The succeeding two centuries saw less church building activity but new styles of decoration were introduced, including the ball flower seen in the cathedral and also at Badgeworth and Bishop's Cleeve. Chancels were often extended to

38 Flaxley Abbey, now a private house, once a remote Cistercian abbey on the edge of the Forest of Dean

house the possessions of the priests and to emphasise their role. Some churches were given saddle back roofs to their towers as, for example, at Syde, North Cerney and Brookthorpe. But the major landscape contribution during this period was the introduction of spires, mostly tall and slender and some broached. They are widely scattered across the county, with two small clusters in the Vale, one at Slimbridge, Standish and Haresfield and the other at Cheltenham, Leckhampton and Shurdington. These spires have required repairs from time to time and some were never replaced after storm damage. In parts of Europe, such as Brittany, church spires are constructed so as to be visible from all parts of the parish but here in the gentle terrain of the Vale visibility goes far beyond the parish boundaries. Many of the bell cotes of small Cotswold churches also date from this time.

As mentioned previously, wool wealth in the fifteenth century brought great prosperity to the Cotswolds. Prices peaked in the 1480s and many wool merchants used some of their wealth to fund the rebuilding of the churches, particularly in the market towns. So the great wool churches of Chipping Campden, Cirencester, Fairford (*39*), Northleach and Winchcombe were erected. Lechlade also has a wool church as do several villages, such as Bledington, Chedworth and Withington. Above all is the exterior of Gloucester Cathedral, where it is

39 St Mary's Church, Fairford. One of the great wool churches of the Cotswolds, rebuilt in the late fifteenth century through the gift of John Tame and incorporating a unique set of medieval stained glass windows

thought the Perpendicular style of architecture began as early as the 1330s. The delicate stonework of the towers with their diagonal buttresses, panelling, pierced battlements and sculptures of human, animal and mythical forms are typical. Roofs were raised and the clerestory windows gave a light and airy interior to the churches. Because the clergy were responsible for the maintenance of the chancels this secular wealth was applied primarily to the naves and towers and, in the case of Cirencester and Northleach, to the south porches. The potential of oolitic limestone for fine carving is exploited to the full in these magnificent buildings. Apart from the memorials to the chief benefactors, the churches also indicate the sources of the wealth. At Northleach the memorial brasses show feet resting on sheep or wool sacks, and at Fairford high on the tower are the carved symbols of shears and scissors. At Chedworth (*40*), on an outside wall and in arabic numerals, is the rebuilding date of 1485.

Exuberant and ostentatious building – 'bribes to heaven' as H.J. Massingham called them – largely ceased with the Reformation and the next important phase of church building occurred in the early nineteenth century in the growing centres of population associated with the industrial development of the Forest of Dean and the Stroud valleys and with the urban growth of Cheltenham.

40 The parish church at Chedworth is also a wool church with the date 1485 carved into a projection on the south wall. The high clerestory windows make the interiors of these churches light and airy and the exteriors have many delicately carved decorative features

Concerns for the welfare of the Forest population came from two clergy in Newland and Mitcheldean. They were responsible for the first churches in the Forest, Christ Church at Berry Hill in 1816 and Holy Trinity, Drybrook, in 1817. Others followed in the new industrial settlements at Cinderford, Parkend and Lydbrook. Churches around the periphery of the Forest such as Staunton, Ruardean, Newland and St Briavel's are much older. The impetus for church building in the Stroud area came from the Revd Thomas Keble, brother of John Keble, and vicar of Bisley. The Kebles and the succession of curates at Bisley were important figures in the Oxford Movement which sought to restore a High Church liturgy. So the architecture of their new churches expressed these ideals. Bussage is possibly the clearest example but the churches at France Lynch, Stinchcombe, and the rebuilt one at Bisley (*41*) with their dark interiors, encaustic tiles and carved figureheads of saints show similar features. Externally, frequent use of crosses as decoration is typical. The rapid growth of Cheltenham in the early nineteenth century led to new churches in the various housing developments, the style of building reflecting the social composition of the neighbourhoods – Christ Church for the affluent of the Bayshill area and St Paul's for the working class. Gloucester already had a number of medieval

41 The church spire at Bisley dominates the houses, including the vicarage. Bisley was a centre for the Oxford Movement of which its vicar the Revd Thomas Keble was a leader

churches and did not grow as rapidly in the nineteenth century as Cheltenham, so there were few additions here at this time.

Many churches were altered or rebuilt in the second half of the nineteenth century but now the appearance of the church depended on the architect chosen to oversee the work, rather than on local circumstances. Among the architects Thomas Fulljames, Sidney Gambier Parry, John Middleton and Francis Niblett may be mentioned as locally based and involved in many buildings. Fine nineteenth-century church buildings include those at Fretherne, Highnam and Huntley and at Selsley G.F. Bodley designed the church with its famous William Morris windows (*colour plate 13*). This church overlooks the tower of Ebley Mill which he also designed for the valley below.

Nonconformity became important in Gloucestershire in the seventeenth century, spreading north from the Bristol area, and by the time of the 1851 census 43 per cent of the church-going population in the county were nonconformists. Two typical early chapels dating from the seventeenth century are the Friends' Meeting House in Nailsworth and the old Baptist Chapel in Tewkesbury (*42*). Dissent was associated with early industrial areas, and the employment structures of the congregations often included frameknitters, weavers, miners, quarrymen and local craftsmen of various kinds. In these areas the Anglican Church was often slow to respond to the growing populations. The preaching of John Wesley and George Whitefield stimulated the formation of cottage meetings and these later led to the building of chapels. In rural areas chapels were more likely to have been built where large parishes had more than one settlement, or where there were several freeholders, whereas in estate villages or squire villages they were less likely. In fact the existence of one or more nonconformist chapels is often a good indicator of an open village in the nineteenth century. In these villages the control by the squire or rector was less than in the other villages where there was sometimes strong opposition to nonconformity. The sermon notes of the Revd Charles Coxwell, vicar of Bibury in 1802, include a reference to the fact that in his opinion England faced two main enemies, the French and Methodists! The architecture of the chapels is usually simple, with size and ornamentation depending on the numbers and wealth of the congregations. Generally Wesleyan chapels were associated with lower-middle class populations and Primitive Methodist chapels with working class people. When the cost of maintenance has become too much for dwindling congregations many of the small chapels in the villages have closed and have been converted to houses, offices and stores. Some fine buildings remain in the towns, however, apart from in Gloucester, where

42 The interior of the old Baptist Chapel at Tewkesbury. Originally a house it was converted to a chapel in the late seventeenth century. Notice the central pulpit and the baptistery under the wooden cover on the floor

most were demolished in the 1960s and 1970s. Two mosques were built in the Barton Street area of the city in the 1980s.

The siting of churches is worthy of comment. The earliest may be on pre-Christian religious sites, such as on hilltops, or at least on the highest ground. A few are on the sites of Roman settlements as at Woodchester and Deerhurst. A circular churchyard is also thought to indicate an old site, as at Hewelsfield and Ozleworth. When the church occupies a plot of land similar in size to the other building plots of a nucleated village it is likely to have been built at the time of the village layout, the date of the church indicating the date of the village plan. Reference has already been made to the grouping of church and manor house – usually a Norman concept. A small church in a farmyard is quite common, where it is often dwarfed by farm buildings, though perhaps not as overwhelmed as by the nineteenth-century mansions such as those at Rendcomb, Sherborne and Cowley. Not infrequently the church is at a distance from the present-day village centre. This is normally because the village has moved and earthworks near the church may indicate the sites of the former houses of the village. In the market towns the church usually adjoins the market place. It occupies a prime site and at one time services were held there on market days.

43 The churchyard at Painswick is noted for its clipped yew trees and for its collection of ornate table-tombs. Many of these were for seventeenth- and eighteenth-century clothiers

The Church was not only responsible for buildings for public worship but was also a major landowner. Produce from its farms and from tithes was stored in its massive tithe barns of which notable examples are found at Ashleworth, Frocester, Hartpury, Postlip, Southam, Stanway and Syde. With the eighteenth-century enclosure movement the Church was often granted land instead of the right to collect tithes from landholders, and it was usually on the edge of parishes that these new and large farms were created. Their buildings date from that of the Enclosure Award. Church Farm, Glebe Farm and Rectory Farm are common names of farms. Rectories were built for the incumbents; two early ones are at Buckland and Withington. The later homes of squarsons were opulent and are now too costly to maintain and too large for the present-day clergy, and many have been sold and replaced by more modest houses. The Church was also responsible for many schools and retains an interest in them today.

Another important landscape feature is the churchyard. Legible gravestones date back to the sixteenth century, their degree of weathering depending on age, exposure and quality of stone. Styles and ornamentation vary and some churchyards, such as Painswick, are famous for their stonework (43). Inscriptions sometimes give details of the occupation of the deceased and the tombs of stonemasons often have stones of the finest quality – as perhaps one might expect.

So for a thousand years and more the landscape has been given its vertical dimension by these fine buildings, to which people have come in joy and sadness, in fact as the hymn puts it 'through all the changing scenes of life.'

7

Landscapes of pleasure and leisure

Although most rural land in the county has been put to economic uses in farming, fruit growing and forestry, some has always been devoted to pleasure and to leisure activities. This may be both in the form of ornamental gardens and landscapes and also in land for sporting and recreational pursuits. Nowadays it is common for these too to have a commercial side, but this was not always the case.

The oldest ornamental garden of which we have visible evidence today lies over the churchyard wall to the south of St James' church, Chipping Campden. Here between two restored pavilions and beside the last remains of the ruins of Sir Baptist Hicks' early seventeenth-century mansion is the upper terrace of the formal gardens he laid out. Below this terrace, earthworks show how the land was stepped down to the eastward flowing Cam Brook besides which rushy hollows and wet channels indicate a less formal water garden. The mansion was destroyed in the Civil War but the outlines of the garden remain. The almshouses in Church Street, the Market Hall in the High Street and the Court House in Calf Lane were all built by Sir Baptist Hicks. The impressive black and white marble monument to Sir Baptist and his wife fills the side chapel of the church.

Another extravagant stone monument is found in the south transept of St Kenelm's church, Sapperton. It is the huge, colourful and flamboyant monument to Sir Robert Atkyns, whose book *The Ancient and Present State of Gloucestershire*, published in 1712, is the earliest county history. The book was illustrated by engravings of the principal seats of the county's gentry by Jan Kip. These engravings of bird's-eye views of the houses also show their gardens and settings. The engravings are stylised and estate enhancing but are still valuable documents for investigating the present day traces of these late seventeenth- to early eighteenth-century gardens. In the case of Sapperton Manor, the home of Sir Robert, we may locate the site of the house from the mounds in the field behind the church. The flat grazed area beside it was the bowling green and Upper Dorvel House probably incorporates the cottage faintly shown in the Kip engraving. A copy of the engraving hangs in the church.

Many old houses and gardens can be identified in this way. They include The Greenway at Shurdington, Flaxley Abbey and Coberley Court. One of the most interesting is at Cassey Compton. Kip presents an oblique aerial view from the south-west. The house shown is much larger than today's. It has a front courtyard with waiting coach and six, which was a symbol of wealth. There is a raised bowling green in the right foreground, beside it a lawn divided into six parts by paths and leading to a circular pool and fountain with exedra, and beyond this and viewed from a raised terrace is an intricately patterned parterre. The canalised Coln separates these areas from the house and the river is crossed by a central bridge. Behind the house are a series of geometrically planned and planted vegetable gardens and orchards. In the left foreground are stables with dormer windows and a dovecote at the end. In the right background is a walled deer park and wooded area with rides converging on a central tree, and in the left background the road to Compton Abdale climbs the side of the hill. It is a splendid view (44). If we visit Cassey Compton today, once we have found our bearings, we notice that only the left side wing of the house and part of the centre remains. The site of the bowling green is mainly occupied by a Dutch barn, the lawn has lost its embellishments but two of the beautifully carved stone vases that cap the pillars in the engraving remain here, and the small clipped yews that lined the raised areas either side of the lawn have now become massive shaggy trees. The ornamental gardens and orchards are now grassed over but some of the divisions may be seen in the grass. The stables with the nesting boxes for doves remain as in the engraving of 300 years ago.

Another important garden recorded by Kip is at Westbury Court. For this garden, further information is available on its construction from the surviving account book of its designer, Maynard Colchester. To better appreciate the elaborate parterres that characterised these gardens it was necessary to look down on them. Sometimes an upstairs window of the house would provide a suitable vantage point, in other cases, as at Cassey Compton, a raised walkway was sufficient, but here at Westbury a tall pavilion enabled a view of the whole garden (colour plate 14). Another common feature of these gardens, well displayed

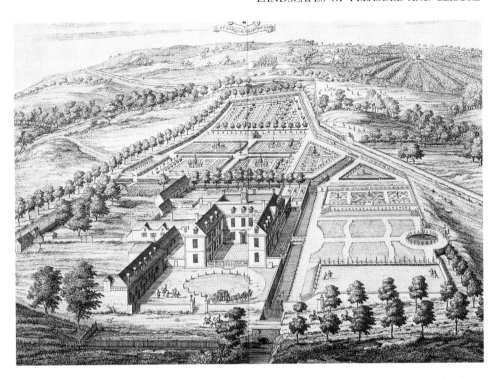

44 Engraving of Cassey Compton House and Garden by Jan Kip and published in 1712. Its details are discussed in the text

at Westbury, is the canal. In the still waters of the canal the topiary work of alternating round hollies and conical yews was clearly reflected, so giving double value to the work of the shearers. Also reflected in the water were the flowers of the very expensive bulbs, such as tulips and lilies, which were fashionable at the time. These gardens were costly to plant and to maintain and where documents survive they indicate that more money was spent on the garden than on the house. At Westbury the house was a very poor second. The National Trust now maintains this garden and only plants that were available at the end of the seventeenth century are grown. The original layout has been restored with minor changes to better illustrate the gardens of the period. The latest feature is a small rabbit warren which the engraving shows close to the road. The water garden is a unique survivor from a time when many country houses had similar layouts. Roughly half of the Kip engravings of country houses had canal features.

About 20 years after Westbury Court Garden was finished, the account book of another family gives further insight into garden expenditure. An old leather bound notebook, that began life as a Greek vocabulary and then continued to be used as a catalogue of library books, was finally used to record various household expenses at Owlpen Manor, near Uley (*30*). After dealing with land tax and window tax, it gives the 'charge of the garden'. The plants bought include peach, apricot and nectarine fruit trees for the walls, 'greens' i.e. evergreens including yews, which were brought from Bristol, and sufficient box plants from Boxwell for 100 yards of edging for the gardens. The south-facing slopes of this sheltered valley would have been suitable for vines as annual temperatures were beginning to rise from their mid-seventeenth-century low levels. Thirty four vines were bought. Also purchased were 24 pinks at 8s and one dozen tulips at 2s. These costs may be compared with the weekly wage of 5s for the miller. In addition to the costs of plants the account book gives details of expenditure on walls, steps and paving. Some of the eighteenth-century framework and a few old yew trees remain in the garden today.

At Painswick House the Rococo Garden has been carefully restored, using as a guide an illustration of the garden painted in 1748 by Thomas Robins. For a brief period in the mid-eighteenth-century rococo gardens, emphasising rocks and shells, were popular. The survival of this particular garden may be partly explained by the unsuitability of the secluded valley at the back of the house for the landscaping fashions that followed later in the century. So the beech trees in the hollow were allowed to grow to maturity and dense undergrowth eventually

45 A view of the famous Rococo Garden at Painswick House, now restored to a likeness of the painting by Thomas Robins of 1748

masked the garden's outline. Since 1984 the Gothic buildings and winding paths have been restored and the diamond-shaped vegetable garden laid out. The geometric patterns of the dogwood and fruit tree plantings replicate those of the painting (45). As at Westbury, care has been taken in the choice of plants to ensure that as far as possible they are authentic to the period of the garden's formation. Its shady walks, colourful vegetable plots, maturing fruit trees and painted summer houses make this a pleasant garden in which to sit or stroll and in February crowds of visitors come to view the banks of snowdrops.

The majority of these intricate, labour intensive, ornamental gardens were soon swept away and replaced by the spacious, open designs of the great landscape gardeners of England, William Kent, Lancelot Brown and Humphrey Repton. None of these designers were personally involved with many gardens in the county although they were very active in the adjoining counties. However, they had numerous followers and the grounds of most country houses were affected by their styles. The sale details of one such small Cotswold country house at Temple Guiting extols 'the fearful precipices, the ornamental water, the never ending peeps, the meandering of the stream below, the delightful inequality everywhere, the cascades and hollow glens, the embowering shades and rock work, the gracefully waving fern scattered over the foreground, imparting such an air of tempered wildness as will gratify the lover of scenery'. This is significantly different from most of the gardens previously described. Repton worked at Adlestrop and Sezincote. His landscaping is characterised by a long winding drive by which visitors could obtain glimpses of the grounds. Shrubs and raised banks obscured the view from sections of the drive and brief openings allowed the succession of views. He often planted more than one tree in a dug out hole and balanced one major specimen tree with a group of smaller ones. Cedar trees were planted near to the houses and artificial lakes and waterfalls were also typical design features. Repton was interested in plants as specimens and attempted to restore flowering plants to gardens. This led eventually to the emphasis on the herbaceous border.

With the Arts and Crafts movement a new idea became fashionable, that of dividing the garden into 'rooms' like those of the house. Each room was distinct in its colours and combination of plants and the rooms were linked to one another by archways through the hedges and walls that separate the divisions of the garden. Rodmarton Manor (46) demonstrates this style as do the two National Trust properties of Snowshill and Hidcote. The large gardens that are frequently open to the public such as at Bourton House, Cerney House, Kiftsgate Court, Misarden Park and Sudeley Castle (colour plate 15) each have several separate divisions with their individual characteristics and at Barnsley House a range of different styles were bought together by the late Rosemary Verey.

46 Gardens at Rodmarton Manor. Here the Arts and Crafts concepts of garden design were well expressed in a series of connected 'rooms', each with their own themes

47 A small cottage garden at Bibury. Notice that this is a cross-passage cottage as discussed in the chapter on houses

Gardens of other sizes also make significant contributions to our landscape. The cottage gardens of the Cotswolds, where the colour of the stonework sets off so many flowers to advantage (47), the well manicured flower beds of Imperial Gardens, Cheltenham (*colour plate 16*), and other municipal parks, and the displays at the many nurseries and garden centres, illustrate this point. Although most plants sold at garden centres are brought in from other parts of the country and from the Netherlands, many of the older establishments originally grew their own plants. The small pockets of light, well-drained soils derived from aeolian deposits were ideal for this purpose and it explains the concentration of old market gardens and nurseries along the Shurdington Road and the Tewkesbury Road from Cheltenham, and in other similarly favoured places.

There are several landscapes associated with unique sporting events in Gloucestershire. Cooper's Hill near Brockworth is the setting for the annual Whit Monday cheese rolling race when contestants chase a Double Gloucester cheese down the treacherous slope, a less sedate activity than that of the dry ski slope on Robinswood Hill opposite. At the end of the same week the Cotswold Olympicks are held on Dover's Hill near Chipping Campden. These games date from 1612 and include a range of ancient physical contests such as shin kicking, cudgel playing and wrestling. The event was stopped in 1851 for reasons of antisocial behaviour and part of the hill was enclosed but in 1951 to celebrate the Festival of Britain it was reinstated and continues today. Another old spectator sport was deer coursing with grey hounds and as a grandstand for this the Lodge Park, Sherborne, was built in 1634. The mile-long area of chase is parallel to the lane leading to the Lodge. In 1550 Newark Park was also built, partly as a viewing platform for the hunting and falconry that took place in the Ozleworth valley below. Large estates had their deer parks by permission of the Crown. The boundaries of deer parks consisted of an inner ditch with broad outer bank and paling fence so that deer could enter the park but not easily escape. The curving earthworks are still clearly evident on the north-west border of Oakley Wood, Cirencester, and also at Sherborne Park and Brimpsfield Park. Smaller estates had rabbits for the meat supply and the low oval-shaped pillow mounds were constructed for rabbit burrows where fashionable ladies used ferrets and nets to catch them. Rabbits are an introduced species and were not as common as today.

The first sport with widespread interest was bowls. Many of the Kip engravings referred to above show bowling greens. None of these survive as playing surfaces but there was an old bowling green at the Bell Hotel in Tewkesbury until recently and now the oldest is probably the green behind the Falcon Hotel, Painswick, which dates from the eighteenth century. Much more recent is the green laid out by the boys of Sir Thomas Rich's, Gloucester in the 1960s. Bowling greens are mainly in the towns but cricket pitches are widely distributed, some on village recreation grounds, others on country estates or company sports grounds and many on independently owned land. Despite the turnover of the rural population in the last three decades, village cricket continues as a traditional English game. While the cost of maintenance of good cricket squares is now outside the state school budget, the two venues for county matches are both on school grounds, those of Cheltenham College and the King's School, Gloucester, the latter replacing Gloucester's Wagon Works ground in the county's fixtures. The market towns all had flourishing clubs 100 years ago and Bourton C.C. still uses its original Victorian pavilion (*48*) which was moved to the present ground in 1923.

The growing popularity of golf, now that it has lost some of its elitist image, has led to new courses being laid out. Most of the earlier courses were on less valuable agricultural land such as along the top of the Cotswold escarpment from Willersey through Cleeve, Ullenwood, Painswick, Stinchcombe to Wotton-under-Edge, or on other less productive or common land as at Minchinhampton and Robinswood Hill. But the decline in agricultural prosperity has changed the economics of farmland and new golf courses are on previously cultivated areas as at Naunton, Shipton and Highham and others are planned. The new courses are

48 The Victorian pavilion of Bourton-on-the-Water Cricket Club

landscaped and as the young trees mature, a wooded appearance will be given to the formerly open farmland. Good natural drainage is a necessity for golf courses and the limestone of the Cotswolds provides this.

Good drainage is also an asset for horse riding. Bibury racecourse on Barrington Downs dates from the seventeenth century. It is marked on Isaac Taylor's map of Gloucestershire and received royal patronage. Racing later moved to Cleeve Common and the lane approaching this from the south via Whittington was made to give easy access to this figure-of-eight course. Tewkesbury Ham and Minchinhampton Common were also early race venues. Nowadays the Cheltenham Gold Cup course at Prestbury Park is of worldwide fame, but popular local point-to-point race courses are at Andoversford and Maisemore. The Cotswolds with their wide open spaces and short springy turf have long been an important area for breeding and training horses. For racehorses the slopes above the Windrush valley from Ford through Guiting Power to Naunton is a significant area (*colour plate 17*); for hunters the stables are much more widespread and the polo grounds in Cirencester Park encourage the rearing and training of polo ponies around Cirencester. Few Cotswold parishes are without their stables, and riding schools have come to the urban neighbourhoods.

49 Spoilt for choice! Well signed and maintained footpaths are now a feature of the Cotswold landscape, thanks largely to the voluntary work of the Cotswold Wardens

Soccer pitches are also widely distributed through the county while rugby football pitches are more common in Gloucester and the Forest of Dean, the Kingsholm ground, home of Gloucester RFC, being pre-eminent.

The disused gravel pits along the lower Severn at Frampton and the upper Thames tributaries at Lechlade and South Cerney have become artificial lakes not only significant for wildlife and of major ornithological interest but also used for angling, sailing and water sports. The number of lakes will increase as gravel extraction continues. Probably the most popular leisure activity is walking and the county has a number of well-marked (*49*) and maintained long-distance footpaths including the Cotswold Way, Severn Way, Gloucestershire Way and the Wysis Way which cross the whole county, the first two from north to south, the latter two from west to east. Other long-distance paths cross parts of the county – mainly the Cotswolds. For cycling the old railway tracks in the Forest of Dean are most popular.

Increased mobility and leisure time have made the countryside much more accessible to the urban populations and landscapes of pleasure and recreation are popular destinations. The fact that this chapter is entitled 'Landscapes of pleasure and leisure' does not imply that other landscapes do not give pleasure or provide opportunities for leisure. Pleasure may be experienced in the working landscapes of field and woods, in the craftsmanship of buildings and in the architectural ornamentation of churches but the landscapes considered here were designed primarily for private or public pleasure and leisure.

8

Villages through the ages

Although many villages have a timeless quality about their appearance and their essential fabric, as seen in photographs and paintings of 50, 100 and more years ago, may show little change from that of today, socially and economically they are very different from earlier times. They began, and continued for many centuries, as centres for local employment based on the resources of the place, mainly in agriculture but sometimes latterly in mining, iron working and textiles. Today, few people living in villages work there, most are retired or commute to work. So the survival of a village, originally based on farming, has depended on its ability to adapt to social and economic changes. Some villages have changed out of all recognition, others show little visible signs of change, others have disappeared completely. In this chapter we will trace the major phases in the development of our rural settlement pattern.

Evidence for the earliest permanent settlements in Gloucestershire comes from the Neolithic long barrows of which about 80 have been identified on the Cotswolds, making this the most important area for long barrows in Europe. Their contents included the bones of sheep indicating a pastoral economy, and stone querns implying corn growing. The large sizes of the long barrows (50) and the fact that the stone implements found in and around them come from far distant places indicate a degree of social organisation. More significant for us is the fact that their dated contents span a thousand years or more. Thus, somewhere

50 A Cotswold long barrow. Typically the long, low mound of a barrow contained one or more stone chambers in which human and animal bones and a variety of artefacts were placed. Long barrows were of significance to the local population for more than a thousand years and are indicators of the earliest permanent settlements

in their vicinity was a resident population of long duration. Standing beside the two most famous barrows, the restored Belas Knap near Winchcombe and Hetty Pegler's Tump near Nympsfield, one cannot guess where the settlements were, but they must have been nearby. Often long barrows are associated with tumuli of the Bronze Age. This again hints at a permanency of settlement and one which could accommodate cultural change.

By the time of the Iron Age we have field evidence of housing. At the hill fort at Crickley excavations have revealed post holes of huts, some rectangular in plan, some circular, which overlap each other. They occur within a triangular area defended on two sides by the steep escarpment and on the third by a substantial man-made rampart. This is clear evidence that people once lived here, but residence may not have been permanent. There are the remains of at least 30 hill forts along the crest of the Cotswold escarpment. In winter their sites are extremely exposed and bleak, being open not only to the prevailing south-westerly winds but also to the cold north-easterlies and they are also some distance from the springs which would have been their water sources. Even allowing for environmental change they are not in the best places for permanent living – unless they were needed for some form of defence. For this their sites were ideal, with good visibility and difficult access for enemy attack. It is likely that they were used when invasion threatened, but in times of peace there were better locations for their agriculture and for their permanent settlements. The latter were possibly on the sites of the sheltered and well-watered present-day villages at the foot of the escarpment.

Iron Age settlement was not confined to the hill forts and their surroundings. At Bagendon there was a more extensive settlement. Here within massive earthworks was a metal working centre producing most delicately crafted ornaments and hardware. The Birdlip mirror, now in Gloucester museum, probably came from here and several brooches in the form of beautifully shaped safety pins have been found in and around Bagendon and have been named after the settlement. There was also a mint, producing gold and silver coins, and the distribution pattern of sites where these coins have been found discloses a trading network of routes to the centres for metal ores including Cornwall, Shropshire, the Forest of Dean and the Mendips for tin, gold, iron, silver and lead respectively. Perhaps exaggerated claims have been made for the significance of Bagendon, but one cannot fail to be impressed by the quality of its metal goods and the degree of luxury to which they point.

In Roman times an organised economy was established in which country estates produced corn and wool for the urban markets. Villas formed the hub of these estates and they were located along the Roman roads, near land suited to both arable farming and sheep grazing, and within a radius of about 7 miles of the towns (51). Outside this distance, transport problems increased and villas are less frequent. As the Roman period continued, the location of villas became more precisely planned than was the case with those that were continuations from Iron Age farms, as at Hucclecote. They were below springs from which water could flow through the villa buildings, and often in places which in later centuries would have been regarded as scenic. They were also at some distance from, and out of sight of, the cultivated land near to which the work force of the estate would have lived for easy access to the fields. There is evidence that some of the present day villages of the Cotswolds are on the site of these workers' settlements, and these are at a distance from the remains of the villas. Withington is the quoted example based on the researches of H.P.R. Finberg but the same is probably true of Chedworth, Witcombe and Whittington. In fact, Roman villas are rarely close to later settlements even though they would have been concerned with cultivating the same land. Finberg thought that the villa estates may have corresponded to the lands of the Saxon manors which followed, and subsequently to parish territories.

51 The setting of a Roman villa. Villas were the centres of corn growing and sheep farming estates and were sited below springs from which water could flow through the premises. They are often in scenically attractive locations. The site of the Dryhill villa is in the centre of the photograph

With the fall of the Roman Empire villas were abandoned and eventually self-sufficient Saxon rural communities were established. For self-sufficiency a community needed access to the basic resources of water, arable land for corn growing, meadowland for hay and cattle grazing, pasture for sheep, wood for fuel and timber and latterly quarries for building stone. The best sites for settlements were those which gave easy access to these resources, and especially to water, arable and meadow land. These were often along geological boundaries where springs occurred and where land on either side had different agricultural potential. So we find settlements developing along the spring line at the foot of the Cotswold escarpment, at the boundary between Great Oolite and Fuller's Earth on the Cotswolds and on the edge of gravel deposits. In the Severn valley another factor was important, that of drainage. Low-lying, heavy clay soils have poor natural drainage and settlements here were sited on the small patches of surface deposits of sand and gravel that are scattered across the valley. Frequently the shape of the village that eventually developed corresponded to the shape of the deposit.

No doubt some sites proved less successful, perhaps through unforeseen problems like flooding, disease, or exposure to storms, and were abandoned and the population moved to other locations. However, by the time of the Domesday Book of 1086 a pattern of rural settlement had been established which is still recognisable today. William the Conqueror's Domesday survey was planned in Gloucester in 1085 and commissioners were sent to circuits of counties to obtain standard information from every vill, i.e. every manor. Their questions covered a range of items including name, value and ownership of the manor, its area, population details, number of plough teams, extent of woodland and of other land uses, and particular details of its economy such as mills, quarries and fisheries. The commissioners had to report back within a year and the information was collated and rearranged at Winchester. Three hundred and seventy nine settlements are named for Gloucestershire and nearly all may be identified from today's place names, although the spelling differs. The manors are evenly spread over the Cotswolds and Vale, but not in the Forest. Because of subsequent settlement reorganisation, we cannot be certain that the Domesday name corresponding to the present-day name refers exactly to the same settlement, but if not, both settlements will have been in the same territorial unit.

Under Norman lords of manors some villages would have been replanned, and sometimes the name of the lord was added to the place name. Where the second word in a double barrel place name is a Norman family name this is likely to have been the case, and the village form may still possess a regularity from that early planned layout. Often the name merely indicates ownership as in Abbot's, Bishop's or King's. Saxon place names applied to villages were descriptive and it would have been possible to recognise the place from its name. For example, the shape of a valley was indicated by a suffix – 'dean' referred to a long, narrow valley and 'combe' to a short, steep valley, whether winding as in Winchcombe, or wide as in Witcombe. The shape of a hill was also described by a suffix – 'don' meaning a low, rounded hill about 70m high and 'cric' meaning a surprise feature. The type of livestock, tree or crop growing in a '-ley' or clearing are recorded in Cowley, Berkeley (birch) and Flaxley, and the farming emphasis in Shipton (sheep) and Whaddon (wheat) are precise descriptions. The names were given by neighbours and some might almost be regarded as derogatory as Quedgeley (a clearing with a rubbish heap) or Slimbridge (a slimey bridge) and once a name was given it stuck to the place even though subsequent people did not understand the meaning. From this we have names characterised by tautology, as in Alney Island meaning 'alder island island' and in Churchdown Hill as mentioned in the introduction. We need to go back to the earliest spellings in order to be certain of the meaning of the place name and guesswork is not advised! Redbrook does not refer to the iron colour of the stream but to its reeds, and neither Brockworth nor Badgeworth refer to badgers!

Reorganisation of settlements frequently occurred in the fourteenth century following the Black Death of 1347-49. Prior to this, place name study suggests that new daughter settlements had infilled the Domesday pattern. As a result of the high numbers of deaths occurring in these three years and at other times of epidemics in the medieval period many settlements were abandoned or shrunken, particularly those that were smaller and more exposed. It is from this time that many of the deserted villages originate. A significant number are on high ground and exposed to the cold north-east winds which were associated with a deteriorating climate in the mid-fourteenth century. This implies that colder springs and wetter summers caused lower yields of corn in these places and an under-nourished population here was more vulnerable to epidemics. There have been many other causes of settlement desertion including soil exhaustion; village removal from land given to Cistercian monasteries as at Hailes, or from the vicinity of country houses as at Sudeley; a change in the farming policy of landowners who moved from corn growing to wool production and therefore needed far fewer labourers; and a movement to a more sheltered position as by the hillside at Whittington. However, Black Death is the most commonly

52 Naunton. Although the village extends for more than a kilometre along a road parallel to the river Windrush, the church, former rectory and many cottages are at one end. The parish boundary follows the lane marked by the hedgerow beyond the church. We would expect a village to be in the centre of its parish and the reasons for Naunton's unusual location are discussed in the text

53 Aylworth. The uneven field beyond the buildings is the site of a deserted medieval village. The field is known as Lady's Hayes. The field in the foreground is Conigree suggesting that the medieval manor of Aylworth obtained part of its meat supply from rabbits and there were probably pillow mounds where rabbits burrowed here at one time

quoted cause. A clear example is at Naunton, where the name originally meant a new farmstead or settlement. The village of Naunton is at the very edge of its parish (52) and therefore in an unlikely position, although it has the advantages of being sheltered on the north, sited on a gravel spread above the valley floor of the Windrush and well supplied by spring water. Within the parish are two deserted villages. At Aylworth, to the south, was a Saxon manor with land exactly corresponding in area to Aylworth Farm when it was sold in the 1920s (53). The earthworks in a field called Lady's Hayes mark the site of a former village – hayes means a hedged enclosure and lady refers to Our Lady, so one presumes there was once a chapel here dedicated to St Mary. The other deserted village in the parish is at Lower Harford – where the bridleway to Bourton crosses the uneven ground of the former village site. After a population disaster the survivors from these settlements would have been gathered together at Naunton to make a viable agricultural community. The same would have happened in many parishes in this area of the county. At Whittington we have an interesting sequence of settlement. In a field adjacent to the A40 road are the remains of a Roman villa, with the untidy mounds of waste left from an excavation. Here, pieces of mosaic floor are

54 Plump Hill above Mitcheldean. Around the iron and coal mining areas of the Forest squatter settlements developed to accommodate the early mining population. Dispersed houses typically face in all directions and are linked by a complex network of tracks and path

sometimes found around the rabbit burrows in the mounds. From the site of the villa a sunken hollow way runs north-westwards between small areas of raised ground where the houses of a medieval village once stood. Across the lane the sixteenth-century Whittington Court is partly surrounded by an earlier moat and rather dwarfs a small Norman church. The modern village lies to the north under a hill, and is either the surviving part of a much larger settlement, or the place to which the village moved to find shelter from cold north-easterly winds.

The next significant development in the pattern of rural settlement of the county came with the requirement of a labour force for industrial processes using water power. In the Stroud area, along the Frome and its tributaries, water power was used to drive textile machinery and in the Forest of Dean water power was used for the bellows of the blast furnaces and the hammers of the forges, as discussed in a later chapter. Local housing was required for the spinners, weavers and iron workers in these industrial districts. Landowners turned a blind eye to illegal settlements on the commons and crown land, and the loose disorganised housing pattern on the former commons at Bisley on the Cotswolds, and near Coleford, Parkend and Bream in the Forest, are typical of squatter settlements (54). Squatter's 'law' stated that if a house could be built and a fire lit in the grate within 24 hours it could be kept, and the area that could be enclosed for a garden was the area over which an axe could be thrown. Speed and strength were the order of the day!

As we have seen, Parliamentary Enclosure Acts also contributed to changes in rural settlement. With the reallocation of land following the Acts some farmers could continue to operate efficiently from their farmsteads in the village. But for many, the distance from their premises in the village to their newly allocated blocks of land was too great for convenience, and so two alternatives were open to them. They could erect a barn and other buildings on their new land from which to work and remain living in the old farmhouse in the village, or they could move completely to the new site. Many farmers did the latter and so across the countryside new farm buildings rapidly sprang up – all dated from the year of the Enclosure Act. The destructive social effect on the village community of this movement must have been great and much village property would have become downgraded.

Another significant nineteenth-century factor in village development was the application of the poor laws. These imposed the responsibility of caring for the poor on the landholders of the parish. Where the parishes were small and with few landholders a dependent poor population was often unwelcome, and the village became closed by retaining a few substantial houses and demolishing the hovels and other properties surplus to the requirements of a basic labour force to work the land. Estate villages become distinctive from this time and may be recognised today by the high quality of the cottages, their uniformity, and the characteristic single dominant colour of the paintwork. On the other hand open villages accommodated poor people and nowadays these villages are larger, more diverse in their house types, and with evidence of tradesmen and craftsmen serving more than just the village population. Nonconformist chapels are more likely here and there was more scope for entrepreneurial activity than in the closed villages. Open villages were also the sources of casual labour for the neighbourhood. Present-day villages with a school, shop/post office, garage, council estate and some modern private estate developments are most likely to have been open villages, while the small showpiece villages were closed villages in the nineteenth century. A comparison of adjacent villages such as Chedworth and Yanworth clearly shows this difference.

Rural populations increased steadily until the mid-nineteenth century, but after this, with depression in agriculture and migration to the growing industrial towns and overseas to New World opportunities, decline set in. This was so serious that J. Arthur Gibbs, writing from Ablington at the end of the century, says of the villages of Winson, Coln Rogers, Coln-St-Denis and Fossbridge, 'Unless there is an unexpected revival ... these old villages will contain scarcely a single inhabitant in a hundred year's time'.

55 Brockworth from Cooper's Hill. The annual cheese rolling race takes place down the steep slope in the foreground. The built up area of Brockworth has spread from the church on the far side towards the junction of the old Roman road Ermin Way and the 1819 turnpike road from Cheltenham to Bath (A46) and beyond. Changes in the types and dates of the housing of the different estates correspond to the former field boundaries. The factory on the left is on the site of the former Gloucester Aircraft Company

Revival came with new forms of transport. First the railway branch lines stimulated growth around the stations and particularly at railway junctions such as Kemble, Andoversford and Ashchurch. Bus services assisted further growth but it has been the mobility provided by private car ownership that has transformed rural communities. Depending on the availability of land for house building and on the decisions of planners, villages close to the main towns have expanded out of all recognition from their pre-Second World War sizes. Often the layout of the modern housing estates corresponds to the earlier field patterns as farmland was built upon in stages. This is apparent when dormitory villages are viewed from neighbouring hills as in the cases of Bishop's Cleeve, viewed from Cleeve Hill, and Brockworth, viewed from Cooper's Hill (55).

Even in remote places there is pressure for new housing as people look for a rural setting for their urban life style. Cottages have been extended, farm buildings and barns have been converted to houses and small-scale infill has occurred. Villages today are no longer the cluster of farms that most were originally, but primarily settlements for the retired and commuters, and with

56 Willersey. An attractive and well kept village built around a green. There was no squire at Willersey and the survival of the green reflects a strong sense of community. Typically ponds, smithies, inns and later schools and village halls were permitted on the green but not private houses

house prices to match. The visible form remains, but the social and economic life has changed. Economies of scale have led to the closure of most village services as the car-owning population seeks a wider and often cheaper range of goods and services in the nearby towns. Only the local service providers, the poor and the less mobile lose out on these changes.

With so many factors influencing village development, it is not surprising that each one is unique, with its own specific history. But the generalisations made in this chapter give a framework into which each one fits. Many villages cluster around the central group of buildings of church, manor and rectory, others are more linear and stretch along a valley floor or historic road as with Naunton and Sherborne, yet others have been built around a village green as at Bledington, Frampton and Willersey (56). Green villages in other parts of the country are associated with pastoral farming and defence. This is less likely in Gloucestershire but these villages still indicate a degree of control over house location, whether it came from a communal decision or the policy of the major landholder (57). They are more common in the east of the county.

57 Guiting Power. Another example of the many green villages in Gloucestershire. The uniform colour of the paintwork of many houses in this village indicates that they belong to the same estate. The war memorial is the only feature allowed on the green

In examining the form of any particular village we usually begin with the various routeways – the roads, tracks and paths. These are normally the oldest elements of the village form and, although today they have different functions, originally they had almost equal significance to the villagers. Within the pattern of these ancient rights of way the old building plots of the village are set. Many of these are at least 800 years old. The individual houses are much more recent and occupy positions in the building plots which may have changed over the centuries, one house replacing another within the same plot. Churches and manor houses are generally the oldest buildings and their sites were more carefully chosen.

Some villages have grown into small market towns and to these we will turn in the next chapter.

9

The rise of the market town

As we have noted earlier, in the Roman economy the surplus produce from the villa estates was transported to the towns and sold there. Villas were therefore located within a radius of about 7 miles from towns such as Cirencester and Gloucester and their produce of wool and corn was carried there to be sold in the forum. The dates of villa building and rebuilding reflect the phases of prosperity brought by the marketing of this produce. Thus when high levels of taxation were imposed in order to support a large Roman army, or when there was competition from imports of cheaper grain from Gaul, villa owners were less prosperous. At other times their increased wealth was expressed in the improved layout of their buildings and in the quality of their mosaics.

The marketing of agricultural products declined in the Saxon period when settlements were largely self-sufficient, although the Domesday Book, which essentially describes late Saxon conditions, records markets at Berkeley, Cirencester, Tewkesbury and Thornbury and there were probably markets in the boroughs of Gloucester and Winchcombe as well.

Once Norman lords of manors had become settled, many realised that to give opportunities on their own land for the sale of surplus produce would provide a new source of revenue in the form of a toll charged on all those who had stalls or standings in the market place and who sold their produce there. They therefore applied to the Crown for the right to establish a market. The main period of market formation was the thirteenth century, but some such as Chipping Campden, Dursley and Stow date from the twelfth century, and a few such as Brimpsfield and Horsley from the fourteenth. Eventually 57 market charters were granted for settlements in Gloucestershire, and as there are 379 settlements recorded in the Domesday survey of the county, about one in seven manors became market places. The produce sold included the surplus from the demesne farm as well as that from peasant holdings, and some was transported for long distances as carrier service to the lord of the manor was one form of peasant obligation. There is documentary evidence from the thirteenth century of carrier service from Buckland to Gloucester, Tewkesbury, Chipping Campden, Evesham and Worcester. The distribution of markets indicates the relative productivity of farmland at the time, with most in the Vale and fewer in the less fertile north Cotswolds.

When the number of applications for markets became too large for zsustainability, an interesting policy for granting market charters was adopted. It was suggested that a carrier walking to market could cover about 20 miles in a day. If the day was divided into three parts, one part walking to market, a second buying or selling at the market and the third returning from market, the maximum convenient distance to travel in both ways was 6.7 miles. Therefore this distance should be the optimum radius of the catchment area for each market. To ensure that the whole land is adequately served, markets should be spaced at about 10-mile intervals. If we follow the Fosse Way, markets were established at roughly this distance apart at Tetbury, Cirencester, Northleach, Stow and Moreton-in-Marsh, although Moreton was too close to Stow to greatly prosper in early times. Both Northleach and Stow were special creations. At Northleach the Abbot of Gloucester allocated 43 acres for a market beside the Fosse Way, and at Stow the market area came mainly from Maugersbury parish. The actual sites for markets were often close to road junctions or bridge points, where suitable space was available, on the land of interested landowners and surrounded by prosperous and varied farming. If they were too close together one usually failed as was the case with Prestbury, which was too near to Cheltenham, and Dymock, which was too near to Newent. The market established at Berkeley in 1070 under the shadow of the castle moved to Newport on the Gloucester to Bristol road in 1348. Where there is an apparent gap in the distribution pattern, it is likely that traces of an old market have disappeared and this is the case with Brimpsfield, close to the road between Gloucester and Cirencester.

The market charter usually gave the day of the week on which the market was to take place and, sometimes, when a fair could be held. Market days were often fixed in conjunction with three other local markets so that traders could follow a circuit of four days. Sometimes the name of a street indicates the market day but the market day occasionally changed. Fairs were important events lasting for a week, and were often fixed around the patron saint's day. As with the famous Stow Fair there were often two in the year. Barton Fair in Gloucester was founded in 1227 and was at least of national importance. There were special commodity locations within the market area for tin merchants from Cornwall, salt merchants from Droitwich, lead merchants from Derbyshire, as well as Italian silk mechants, Flemish cloth merchants and local suppliers of corn, wool and iron. Some markets acquired a reputation for particular types of produce, Cirencester and Cheltenham for corn, Gloucester and Tewkesbury for fruit and hops, Stow for sheep, Tetbury for butter and cheese and Winchcombe for horses.

Two of the county's market towns were primary, i.e. of Roman origin, most grew from villages, and a few were newly planted. But they all developed a characteristic layout which may be recognised in today's town plan. There was a large open space for the market, which may have been a wide street, or a distinct market square (58). Around this were laid out the burgage plots. These were long, narrow strips of land running from the market to a back lane. The plots were 10-20ft wide, with standard widths for the original layout of each

58 The Market Place at Cirencester viewed from the adjoining church tower. A weekly street market is still held here

market town. On these plots the burgesses, i.e. those who had market access rights, built their house, shop and workshop and planted their orchards and gardens. Old prints and many existing buildings show that most houses had their gable ends to the street. There were specialist buildings such as a market hall or other structure in which butter and cheese were sold, a weighing beam, a bell which was rung at the commencement and ending of the market, and numerous inns. Business transactions continued in the inns after the markets closed. Craftsmen came to live in these towns and occupied the burgage plots. Gloucester has a unique record in the form of a property rental for 1455 in which the name of the occupier, his or her trade, and the rent charged are given for 900 properties, of which 46 are shops. It is likely that in the smaller market towns many residents were employed in agriculture and by the time of John Smith's *Men and Armour of Gloucestershire*, published in 1608, 37 per cent of Painswick's working population was still involved in farming. Grammar schools were also a later characteristic feature of these towns; many were founded in the sixteenth and early seventeenth century, with buildings remaining in Gloucester,

59 The Market Hall at Chipping Campden was built by Sir Baptist Hicks in 1627. In it butter and cheese were sold and probably other produce such as poultry. The wide street with well-marked burgage plots on either side is a typical market town layout

60 The Market House at Tetbury dates from 1655. The upstairs hall is supported by two rows of massive pillars. It was originally built for the sale of wool and yarn

Chipping Campden, Stow and Winchcombe. There was usually a church beside the market place, as at Cirencester. In the market towns there were greater and more conspicuous social divisions in the population than in the villages, and correspondingly more varied housing.

Many of our attractive small towns still possess some, or most, of these distinguishing features of market towns. In many cases the width of the old burgage plots can be identified from the length of shop frontages, which are the same as, or multiples of, the burgage plot widths, although the frontages have often been extended into the street. Burgage plots are very clear at Chipping Campden, Moreton-in-Marsh and Wotton-under Edge and traceable in all the towns. Market Halls can be seen at Chipping Campden (*59*), Dursley, Minchinhampton, Newent and Tetbury (*60*), and there is a toll board by the Curfew Tower at Moreton-in-Marsh (*61*). Market squares exist at Fairford, Northleach, Minchinhampton and Stow (*62*), and wide streets elsewhere.

The three wide main streets in Tewkesbury (*63*) were each used for marketing, Church Street for sheep, the upper High Street for cattle and the lower High Street for corn, and Barton Street for general traders such as hatters, coopers and tanners.

61 There is a market toll board on the side of the Curfew Tower at Moreton-in-Marsh

62 The Market Square, Stow on the Wold. Formerly the large square had no island buildings and thousands of sheep were sold here. Many inns adjoined the square. Notice the four gables of the King's Arms. The inn occupies two former burgage plots

Markets prospered in the twelfth and thirteenth centuries, declined with the Black Death in the fourteenth, and experienced a resurgence in the sixteenth and seventeenth centuries when new buildings were erected. Disparity of town sizes came with improved transport, and especially with the arrival of the railways in the nineteenth century. This favoured the larger towns, while the smaller ones to which railways came late, or not at all, suffered.

At the present time widespread car ownership, the growth of out-of-town supermarkets, the confined premises with restrictive building regulations in the town centres and populations below the threshold for modern economic viability have all worked against the prosperity of the old market towns. However, they are now recognised to be attractive places in which to live and have become centres for local planned development. A limited amount of modern housing is allowed and small business parks have been created to give employment opportunities. The existing infrastructure is judged to be suitable for such modest growth. Some, such as Chipping Campden, have become tourist centres, Stow specialises in antiques and the various outlets of Scotts, Tetbury benefits from the Prince of Wales' insignia and Cirencester and Tewkesbury are large enough for a few nationwide shops. Fairford, Newent, Northleach, Painswick and the others

63 A view of Tewkesbury from the Abbey tower. Church Street crosses the foreground and the rear of Abbey Cottages may be clearly seen. The Ham is under water as is often the case in winter and the risk of flooding at the junction of the Severn and Avon has confined the town to a slightly raised terrace

have limited services, although the first two have secondary schools. It is difficult to appreciate that Alkerton, Deerhurst, Newport and Guiting Power once had market charters.

Not all small towns began as market places. We shall consider in a later chapter the industrial towns of the Forest such as Coleford and Cinderford, and the woollen towns of the Cotswolds such as Stroud and Nailsworth, which did not have market charters. Neither did Bourton-on-the-Water, although Samuel Rudder writing in 1779 says 'nature has been lavish with her favours to this place', and he praises its shops and the walk along the banks of the River Windrush. Bourton has become the major tourist honeypot of the Cotswolds (*colour plate 18*). The railways brought visitors, and the disused railway station still remains, but it was the advent of coach trips and later private car ownership that led to the crowds arriving at summer weekends. Bourton then becomes like a seaside resort, with children paddling in the river, families picnicking on the green, ice-cream sellers and fish and chip shops busy with customers and with a growing number of attractions and shops to cater for all ages. It is a very

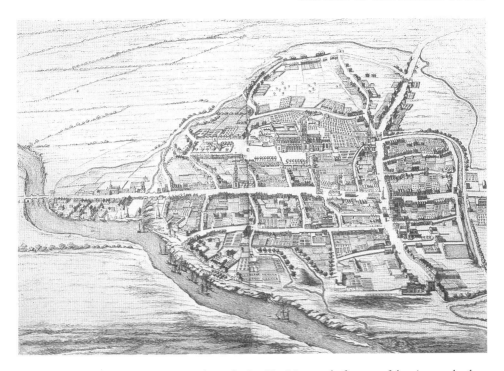

64 The layout of Gloucester in 1712 as drawn by Jan Kip. Many early features of the city are clearly visible including the cathedral, castle and adjacent port. The raised causeway to Westgate Bridge, the changed direction of the street at the north gate, and the market buildings in the main streets are also shown

successful tourist centre and, in attracting such large numbers of people, protects the many other nearby scenic spots with fewer facilities from being overrun with holidaymakers.

Westgate was the principal market street in Gloucester. Its wide layout allowed several buildings to be erected in the middle of the street, including the King's Board, a butter and cheese market house now moved to Hillfield Gardens in London Road; two churches, Holy Trinity and St Mary de Grace; as well as the Booth Hall. There were other market buildings in Eastgate and Southgate. The Kip engraving of the city in 1712 (*64*) clearly illustrates the layout.

But Gloucester was always more than a market town. The original Roman garrison was at Kingsholm and Ermin Way went straight to it. When the new site of Glevum was chosen, the road was extended from Kingsholm to the north gate of the colonia and later this road was bypassed by what has become London Road, which became the main approach road and was lined by the tombs of important citizens. The Roman layout of Gloucester with its four main streets, surrounding wall and gates, gave a framework for the city, although the tenth-century redesign is the basis for today's street pattern. Gloucester became the lowest bridge point of the Severn, where Alney Island made it possible to use two small bridges to cross the river, rather than the one large bridge which would have been necessary both upstream and down. It was also near the tidal limit of the Severn, so shipping could use the incoming tide to reach Gloucester and return on a later ebb tide. The existence of a port and a bridge crossing gave good commercial opportunities and a castle was built to defend them, a pattern repeated in many similar locations in England – most notably in London. With its important monastic establishments and political significance it became a leading city, ranked eighth in the country in the twelfth century. Pin making and bell founding became important occupations, in addition to those in the Church, administration and commerce. With the completion of the Gloucester –Sharpness Canal in 1827 and the associated docks and warehouses, timber works and grain milling were stimulated, and the arrival of the railways brought further industrial development. The restored warehouses and the magnificent cathedral still form major elements in Gloucester's urban landscape (*colour plate 19*) but for many traces of its distinguished history one has to scratch beneath the surface. Basements and attics in the four old streets are often the best places to begin. Some historic buildings have been lost through short-term expediency and there are areas of the old city and its immediate periphery where restoration is badly needed.

Beyond the terraced housing off Barton Street, which was once a fashionable residential area with its fine bow-fronted houses, and off the Bristol Road suburban estates spread north, east and south, incorporating earlier settlements and also some of the later industrial sites. The flood plain of the Severn to the west has curtailed growth in this direction.

Cheltenham's market charter was granted in 1226 and the town was described by Leyland in the early sixteenth century as 'a longe towne havynge a market'. It was in fact a single street until the spa developments of the late eighteenth century. The street was winding, with burgage plots on either side and a market house in the centre, close to the present entrance to Regent Arcade. Following the discovery of the saline springs and the five-week visit of George III, Cheltenham experienced rapid growth, at a rate exceeding that of the industrial towns of the Midlands and the north of England. Eventually more than eight spas were exploited. Typically each had a pump room – two remain at Montpellier and Pittville – where the waters were taken, and a promenade, where the elegant fashions were displayed. Montpellier Walk was the enclosed promenade for its spa (*65*) and the Promenade in front of the Queen's Hotel was that for the Sherborne Spa. The dispersed pattern of spas accounts for the spacious layout of the town as well as the lack of a coordinated road system.

65 Montpellier Walk, Cheltenham. The portico of the domed pump room is at the end of the walk which is lined on the right with shops built in the 1840s and 1850s. The white caryatids may be seen decorating the buildings. Formerly this was a walk enclosed by hedges for those who had taken the spa waters in the pump room

Nurseries were necessary to provide plants for the various walks, and both Imperial Gardens and Montpellier Gardens originated in this way; tree-lined streets are still a major feature of Regency Cheltenham. Hotels were built to accommodate visitors and, although the Plough and the original George Hotel have gone and have been replaced by Regent Arcade and Marks and Spencer respectively, the buildings of the Imperial Hotel (66), now Ottakar's bookshop, and the Clarence Hotel, now John Dower House, remain. Assembly Rooms, theatres and libraries served the growing population of residents and visitors. The ornate shop frontage of Jones, the bootmaker, is derived from its earlier function as a library. Speculative purchase of land at Montpellier and Lansdown in 1801 and the availability of land at Pittville following the Enclosure Acts of 1801 and 1806 led to extensive housing developments in these areas. Within a few years the red brick appearance of the town with its single market street had been completely changed as the Regency style of stone and later stucco-faced, large terraced housing spread.

66 This shop in the Promenade, Cheltenham, was built as the Imperial Hotel in 1823. To appreciate the architecture of town centre buildings it is advisable to view them from the opposite side of the street in order to see above the shop frontages

The spa development also attracted an affluent retired population and hence a number of high class shops. These came first to the High Street and the Colonnade and later to the east side of the Promenade, while the west side was residential. The type of goods sold in these shops has changed over the years but there has always been an emphasis on more expensive items. Schools and the Teacher Training College founded in the mid–nineteenth century partly through the influence of the rector, the Revd Francis Close, have also continued to contribute to the visual appearance of Cheltenham. The most conspicuous building, 13 storeys high, is that built for Eagle Star in 1968. In the 1960s and 1970s Cheltenham attracted considerable office development, particularly associated with finance. Most of the genuine Regency property near the town centre has been preserved through this development and more recently similar property further out has been renovated for comfortable living. However, there have been tendencies for modern buildings to clash violently with their surroundings, or to be rather insipid copies of the Regency style.

A policy of encouraging housing infill is benefiting the appearance of Cheltenham as derelict land is acquired for town houses, and in Gloucester a major housing development is occurring in the area of the docks, but there is constant pressure for urban expansion on to greenfield sites. The landscapes of the urban periphery of ring roads, out-of-town supermarkets, industrial estates, office buildings and modern hotels, although functional and in some cases with individual buildings of character, are not related to the local scene (*colour plate 20*).

10

Traces of the old industrial landscapes

For thousands of years sheep have grazed on the Cotswolds. Evidence for this includes sheep bones in long barrows, Iron Age brooches from Bagendon designed to clasp woollen cloaks, Roman sculptures and mosaics showing similar cloaks, and from the third century the first documentary details of woollen exports.

Expansive sheep walks, well-drained land and calcareous grassland were all favourable to sheep grazing and the animals were multi-purpose, providing not only wool and meat but also manure. They improved the soil by trampling, added manure when they were folded at night, and by nibbling at the springing wheat encouraged tillering and so more stems per plant.

The fleeces of the early sheep consisted of both wool and hair, and the soft under wool was collected by plucking. Once selective breeding had eliminated the hair, shearing became possible and from Roman times onward this was the practice. The traditional Cotswold breed was eventually developed and there are strong similarities between the sheep represented on the wool merchants' brasses in Northleach church and this breed. The animals are tall, with distinctive ringlets on their noses and the medium staple wool hangs to give a parting along their backs (*22*). These were the animals that produced the wool for export in the fourteenth and fifteenth centuries and brought wealth to the merchants. This wealth was displayed in their houses and in the rebuilding of the churches of the market towns. There was some small-scale manufacture of woollen cloth at the time but this was in the main towns such as Gloucester, Tewkesbury and Cirencester.

The major industry of the Stroud valleys did not develop until the late sixteenth century. In John Smith's *Men and Armour of Gloucestershire* of 1608 a list is given not only of the names of men suitable for bearing arms of different sizes but also their occupations. For the county as a whole 15 per cent of the men listed were employed in the woollen industry and in Bisley Hundred, which included Stroud, Painswick and Bisley, the figure was 39 per cent. The industry was very important until the nineteenth century and has left its mark on the landscape here.

The industry was managed by clothiers and the production process was as follows. Wool was brought in from their own flocks, or bought directly from farmers or at the wool markets at Cirencester and Tetbury, and also imported from Spain through the port of Bristol. It was then washed at the mill. The clean water of the Frome and its tributaries, fed by springs and so filtered through the rocks, was an asset. Drying took place in round houses, known as stove houses. A number of these remain, the most conspicuous being the one converted to a house close to the A46 at Woodchester (*colour plate 21*). After this, the wool was oiled and distributed to the spinners who worked independently. In their cottages on the hillsides above the mill the wool was carded or combed to separate the fibres and then spun by hand. Most of this work was done by women and children. The yarn was then sized with a weak glue, cut to length, and redistributed by the clothiers to the weavers. Weaving was also a cottage industry and some cottages still have the large windows in the attic or, in later buildings, on the ground floor. This allowed more light to reach the hand looms. The cloth was returned to the mill where it was again scoured to remove the size and oil before fulling. In this process the cloth was slowly beaten in water for many hours to give it a felt appearance where the warp and weft were no longer visible. Fulling required water power, so that the rotation of a water wheel could move the cams and wooden mallets on the axle shaft – hence the riverside location of the mills. The surface of the cloth was then roughed by teazles, at first by hand and in latter years in a water driven gig mill, and a final shearing gave a smooth uniform product. Some cloth was sold at this stage, some was dyed. Locally grown woad and imported madder, cochineal, indigo and crushed tropical wood fibres were the main dyes used. The famous red or scarlet cloth from Stroud and the blue cloth from Uley were produced in this way. After dyeing the cloth was hung out on racks to dry. A late eighteenth-century landscape painting of Stroud, now in the museum there, shows the scarlet, yellow, blue and undyed cloth hung on tenter hooks in a field above Wallbridge mill (*colour plate 22*). Such fields were

67 Loveday's Mill, Painswick. The seventeenth-century clothier's house to the right is attached to a large woollen mill rebuilt in about 1825

known as rack closes. The cloth was then sold with the clothier's mark, often incorporating his initials, a shepherd's crook and a cross. These marks were highly valued and some can still be seen on the doorways of the clothiers' houses and on their tombs.

There were, therefore, two types of location for the industry. Beside the streams where water power was available for fulling and gigging were the mills, and also the warehouses for storing wool and cloth, the dye houses and often the clothier's house. Good examples are Loveday's Mill (67) and King's Mill in the Painswick valley. To ensure adequate water power the streams were dammed, or ponds dug out, and sluice gates were installed to control the flow of water from the mill ponds along the mill leats. Some ponds remain, but most have been drained or have silted up. Then, on the former common land high above the valley floor were the squatter cottages of the spinners and weavers. The loosely scattered settlements such as Eastcombe, Bussage, Oakridge, Chalford and Nailsworth originated in this way, although there have been many subsequent changes to property and layout. Along Vicarage Street and Tibbiwell Lane in

68 Restoration work on an early weaver's cottage at Leonard Stanley

Painswick were other cottages of these workers. At Leonard Stanley along the Street in front of St Swithin's Church, and next to a colourful group of buildings, is a sixteenth-century half-timbered weaver's cottage (*68*).

To connect the mills and the homes of the spinners and weavers' paths and tracks were formed down the steep valley sides, and pack animals were used to carry the materials. To transport the rolls of cloth from the mills towards the markets, which were often overseas via the ports of Bristol and London, wagons were necessary and the tortuous roads for these wagons were above the spring line on the valley sides. This dense network of paths, tracks and lanes still exists. The turnpike roads along the valley floors were not developed until the nineteenth century.

In the early nineteenth century both spinning and weaving were transferred to the mills, and here spinning machines and power looms driven by the water wheels were installed. So the old one- or two-storey mills were replaced by much larger ones with four or five floors. Nearly all the mills were rebuilt between 1800 and 1820. Ebley Mill near Stroud, and Dunkirk and Egypt Mills at Nailsworth are typical of these (*colour plate 23*). In some cases, as at King's Stanley, brick was used rather than stone and roofing was of Welsh slate rather than Cotswold stone. Many of the self-employed spinners and weavers were now without work and suffered extreme poverty. This lead to rioting and social unrest. Unemployment was particularly significant in places where it was difficult to obtain coal when steam power eventually displaced water power. Mills along the Stroudwater Canal had good access to Forest of Dean coal but the situation was different in the northern tributary valleys of the Frome towards Painswick and Bisley. Here the industry ceased long before the end of the nineteenth century, although some of the mills were put to such alternative uses as the manufacture of walking sticks, paper clips and hair pins.

The legacy of the industry is of large, rather gaunt mills in varied conditions of repair depending on their subsequent uses – some of which have been beautifully adapted for office and commercial use – as well as dispersed housing along the steep hill sides with a complex pattern of narrow lanes and tracks, many fine seventeenth- and eighteenth-century former clothiers' houses, traces of ponds, leats and dams along the valley bottoms and collections of ornate clothiers' tombs in the churchyards (*43*).

We now turn to the other area of the county notable for its industrial past. With accessible reserves of iron ore and extensive oak woodland to provide charcoal for smelting it, the Forest of Dean became widely known as a potential iron producer. There was an industry here in Roman times and again in the medieval period when iron making took place in many scattered small-scale furnaces known as bloomeries. Deposits of slag once marked these sites, but the bloomery slag still contained much valuable iron and so has been reused.

Industrial sites became more localised and permanent when water power was used to drive the bellows of the furnaces and the hammers of the forges. Blast furnaces were introduced to Britain from the continent in the late sixteenth century. Those built in the Forest were stone structures, about 20ft square at the base and 20ft high, slightly tapering upwards and with a framework of oak and iron beams. The interior had a bottle-shaped cavity into which a charge of iron ore, charcoal and latterly cinders was tipped from above. The ore was pre-heated and broken to small lumps before smelting. Cogs on the axle shaft of the water wheel operated the leather bellows which forced air into the furnace. The molten iron was tapped and the scum removed, to produce slag, and the iron solidified in sand-lined troughs to make the sows of pig iron, or in moulds to make cast iron plates, fire backs and other products.

The introduction of blast furnaces to the Forest came later than to the Weald in south-east England and depended on people with wealth and sufficient influence with the Crown to obtain the necessary concessions of wood, ore, slag and building materials. In 1612 there were four 'King's' iron works. They were located at Lydbrook, Parkend, Soudley and Cannop. Routeways were necessary

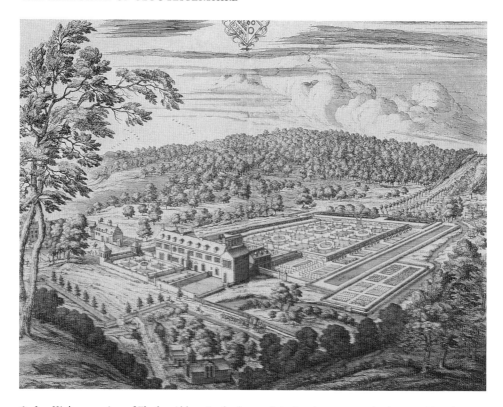

69 Jan Kip's engraving of Flaxley Abbey. In the lower right-hand corner smoke is seen rising from a blast furnace

for access to ore and charcoal but the primary location factor was water power. Streams were dammed to regulate the flow of water and the furnaces were built close to the steep valley sides to enable them to be charged more easily.

The pig iron from the furnace had a high carbon content which could be removed by reheating and hammering at the forge. Hammering was a long and continuous process, so the forges required more water power than the furnaces and were therefore positioned further downstream. There was no need for a steep valley side but hammer ponds were vital. Eventually the valleys of the Lydbrook, Redbrook, Soudley, Cannop and Flaxley streams were heavily industrialised with furnaces and forges, and filled with columns of dark smoke and the noise of massive hammers. The Kip engraving of Flaxley Abbey, published in 1712, shows a blast furnace and forge in the abbey grounds (69) and the modified remains of a blast furnace with cast iron beams, dated 1683, can be seen today at Gun's Mill further up the Flaxley valley.

Water power continued in use until the nineteenth century, the last being at Parkend in 1827 where the furnace was supplied by a leat running from the lower Cannop pond. A few ponds remain but, as in the case of the Stroud valleys, most have silted up and in some cases the land has been drained. Eventually steam power replaced water power for producing the blast at the furnace and for the forge hammers, so a streamside location was no longer necessary as coal could be brought by plateway or railway. And when, in 1795, coke was first used to replace charcoal at Cinderford Iron Works, access to woodland was no longer a requirement. So a new pattern of industrial development ensued around the two centres of Cinderford and Coleford under the influence of the Crawshays and Mushets respectively. The remains of a coke blast furnace dated 1804 stands at Whitecliff (70), south-west of Coleford, and at Darkhill is a selection of industrial archaeological features of great significance in the history of iron smelting. Here, below a small dammed pond are the exposed footings of the Darkhill Iron Works of 1818 (*colour plate 24*). An old railway line, now a cycle track, cuts off a corner of the site, while a short distance to the north-west was the site of the Titanic Steel Works. The Easter iron mines were to the west and an old plateway led to coal mining levels and stone quarries to the east. Lumps

70 Remains of a coke blast furnace at Whitecliff near Coleford. It bears the date 1806 and was for a time worked by the Mushets. Notice its location against higher ground from which the furnace could be fed

of slag are abundant and a nearby garden wall is capped by them. It used to be possible to find pieces of iron ore and other minerals by the footings of the walls. Another site rich in industrial history is the valley bottom immediately to the west of Cinderford. Here an industrial trail with information boards has been laid out in the Linear Park. The information boards use a reproduction of the 1879 OS map and mark the sites of former collieries, iron works and especially the complex network of old railway lines. The area is now a wildlife conservation area with ponds, pine plantations and open grassland but it is still possible to trace the old lines of communication of canal, plateway and railway and the uneven ground where heavy industry once employed hundreds of workers. Other metals besides iron and steel were also worked in the Forest and these include tin plating at Redbrook and the manufacture of copper wire at Lydbrook.

Associated with these furnaces and forges and the metal working that followed are the settlements for the workforce. As in the case of the Stroud woollen industry, the people were originally squatters and the same loose and disorganised housing pattern spread over the hillsides.

Whereas some of the woollen mills could be adapted for other uses, the industrial buildings of the Forest were not so flexible. However, the road network and industrial infrastructure could be used, and with the closure of the iron and steel industry, largely as a result of competition from South Wales, there was a redundant workforce which was locally available for new enterprises. So around the industrial settlements new factories were built at Cinderford, Coleford, Lydney and Mitcheldean and more recently industrial estates have been established in these places. The less accessible valleys and those in the interior of the Forest have been spared this redevelopment, and here the old industrial remains lie hidden in the woodland.

The older towns of Gloucestershire also have an industrial heritage. There were many iron foundries in Gloucester and its traditional industries included bell founding – hence Bell Walk, pin making and at the docks and along the Gloucester and Sharpness Canal, flour milling and timber firms. Famous among the latter was the Moreland match factory. Near Gloucester and Cheltenham were aircraft factories, an interest that remains in the establishments of Dowty and Smiths, although most of the aircraft sites have been put to other uses. Tewkesbury possesses a former hosiery factory now converted to housing. Chipping Campden and Blockley retain the buildings of old water-powered silk mills, which in the nineteenth century supplied silk thread for the ribbon factories in Coventry.

The pattern of industrial decline and factory closure, followed by redevelopment of the site and the arrival of new footloose industries which are able to use the infrastructure and an available labour force, has been repeated frequently and operates today. However, a good communication network is now the single most important location factor.

11

Roads, tracks, paths and canals

As we look west from any high point on the Cotswold edge between Crickley Hill and Coaley Peak our eyes are soon attracted to the movement of traffic on the M5 motorway as it speeds through the county. If then we turn back to our OS map we see much more than the thin blue stripe symbolising the motorway. There is a fine network of roads, tracks and paths by which almost every field and wood, house and village, town and workplace is made accessible. This intricate pattern of routeways has developed from a prehistoric base over more than two millenia of modifications, additions and subtractions. This chapter considers the successive stages in the development of the pattern.

Roman roads served two purposes. One was to enable cohorts of soldiers to travel rapidly to places where they may have been needed, and the other was for carrying goods to market in the Roman towns. Every villa estate required road access to town for the sale of its produce. These roads did not need to be of the straight military type, and in most cases would have been previously used trackways. The villas were located either side of the road, often in pairs, with the road forming the boundary between the two estates, a function that in places continues with today's parishes. Examples of this are the White Way which made Cirencester accessible to the villas at Chedworth and Withington, and Ermin Way which allowed produce from the villas at Witcombe and Dryhill (51) to be taken to Gloucester. Goods which were carried along these roads, other than the corn and wool we have mentioned earlier, included stone roof tiles and flagstone floors of Old Red Sandstone, which came from the Forest of Dean and were popular in Cotswold villas, and pig iron from the Forest, which was widely used in the country. This again implies a well-developed road system – but the short stretch of Roman road at Blackpool Bridge looks almost too good to be true.

The strategic military roads were in straight sections and, as they were aligned from hilltop to hilltop, sometimes change direction slightly at these points. They were well built with compacted gravel and clinker and had stone sets. Some, such as Ermin Way from Silchester through Cirencester to Gloucester and the Fosse Way from Exeter to Lincoln form the basis of modern roads. Others, as with Akeman Street and Ryknild Street are only used in part by modern transport, elsewhere their alignment may be followed by hedgerows, wood boundaries, footpaths and bands of dry shallow soil. There is a very clear example of the latter running west from Halfway Bridge near Birdwood, and shallow cuttings show where Akeman Street crosses a dry valley south of Bibury and the valley of the River Leach near Eastleach Turville (71).

71 Akeman Street where it crosses the valley of the River Leach. The blocks of stone in the foreground are sets from the Roman road which is marked by the line of lighter coloured grass making for the gap in the trees. On the slope to the left are the faint outlines of Celtic fields, the terracing near the valley floor on the right is much more recent

Such well-built Roman roads continued in use for centuries, but they served mainly local needs in Saxon times. The largely self-sufficient Saxon manors merely required access routes from the nucleated villages to the common arable fields and pastures. Such routeways were flexible and complex because each strip of arable land had to be reached by plough teams from the village. However, to reach the pastures and woods beyond the arable fields, more permanent tracks were used, and Saxon charters frequently refer to such well-marked tracks in their descriptions of perambulations around grants of land. In the case of the charter for feld (field, or pasture) at Hawling, dated c.980, reference is made to a grenan wege (green way), a milnstig (mill path) and the sealt straet (salt way). The Salt Way crossed the land at Hawling on its way from the brine sources at Droitwich in Worcestershire to Lechlade at the head of navigation on the Thames. Salt was carried by packhorse along this road, and then taken by boat to London where it was used for curing fish and meat. Many place names along the road contain the word salt, as for example Salters Hill and Saltway Farm. Green ways were often sheep drove roads linking summer and winter pastures. They occur all along the face of the Cotswold escarpment, where summer pastures were on the higher

72 Greenway Lane, a sunken trackway which probably originated as a sheep drove road in the eighth century

ground and the animals were wintered at the foot of the escarpment. Centuries of use by hoofs and wheels, and the erosive effects of spring water running down the tracks in winter have produced sunken ways, now damp, shady and sheltered, green with ivy, dogs mercury and ferns during the spring and brambles and nettles in late summer. Greenway Lane (*72*), a section of the route from Badgeworth to Pinswell which linked the sheep grazing areas belonging to St Peter's Abbey in Gloucester, is a well-known example. Because the tracks to the edges of the Saxon manor estates were independently planned, their alignment was not always ideal when the time came for using them to link settlements. This is the reason that later roads often change direction slightly at parish boundaries. It should be remembered that with all these early routeways the paths, tracks and roads were of equal significance to most users who travelled on foot.

With the development of markets, particularly in the thirteenth century, roads to market became important again and radiating patterns of roads connected the market places to their surrounding villages. Long-distance routes for the export of Cotswold wool were also used. The great wool collecting centres of Chipping Campden, Cirencester and Northleach were linked to the ports at Dover and Southampton. Campden Way was one of these routes. Local tracks, such as Packers' Way at Bibury, were used for assembling the wool, in this case probably at Arlington Row which was once a wool store for Osney Abbey. Bridges across the rivers were also built at this time. Some were simple clapper bridges while others of greater architectural accomplishment had pointed arches. Most of the arched bridges have been repaired and rebuilt several times, but a few retain their original form. Both King John's Bridge across the Avon at Tewkesbury and St John's Bridge across the Thames at Lechlade were built in the early thirteenth century and have been restored in this way. Clapper bridges may be seen at Eastleach (*colour plate 25*), Kineton and Edgeworth.

This was also a time when pilgrimages were popular and, although many pilgrims travelled to Gloucester Cathedral to the shrine of Edward II and to Winchcombe Abbey to the shrine of St Kenelm, it was to the Cistercian Abbey at Hailes that thousands came to see the shrine containing the reputed relic of Christ's blood. The track down to Hailes from the hillside above still shows a neat pattern of stone sets designed to make it usable in all seasons and to prevent gullying, for which it has been most effective.

By an Act of Parliament of 1555 the responsibility for maintaining roads fell to the parishes through which the road passed. Householders were required to provide six days of labour each year for this purpose, either working in the quarries, stone breaking, or road mending. As long as traffic was local this was a reasonable duty, but when through traffic predominated, road maintenance became a heavy burden for the parish. The eventual outcome was the formation of turnpike trusts which charged tolls for road use and thereby financed road maintenance and repairs. The first of the county's turnpike roads was from Gloucester to the top of Crickley Hill, adopted in 1697.

An array of new roadside features now appeared. Toll houses with three-sided fronts and windows for collecting the tolls were built beside the toll gates. On them boards displayed the charges for each type of user. Milestones were erected and at important road junctions there were sign posts. A few toll houses remain but most have been demolished in modern road widening programmes. A toll house with its board stands at Butterrow near Stroud (73) and a similar restored one exists at Oxenton. Green Farmhouse in Lower Oddington uses as its entrance a toll gate, presumably moved from the main road (74). Many surviving milestones are marked on the OS maps. Each turnpike trust had its own shape of milestone and there are a few unusual ones, such as that at Bull's Cross near Painswick where several old roads met. Their metal plates, with the names of the towns and the mileages to them, have mostly gone but some have the names engraved in the stone (75). The county possesses two historic sign posts. At Teddington Hands is a stone pillar with six arms, first erected in 1676, and south-west of Chipping Campden is Nathaniel Izod's finger post of 1669 which is

73 The toll house at Butterrow, near Stroud. This was built in about 1825 and its toll board includes the names of all the different types of horse drawn vehicles for which tolls were charged

74 A former turnpike gate now sited at a farmhouse in Oddington

75 A typical milestone on a turnpike road. This one is at Bisley showing 10 miles to Gloster. Old spellings are common on milestones

76 Nathaniel Izod's finger post near Chipping Campden. This is the oldest surviving sign post and is dated 1669

claimed to be the oldest in the country (76). Inns for the night's accommodation of travellers, and where horses could be changed, were positioned at regular intervals along the turnpikes and at the summits of hills. Many ponds were dug by the roadsides from which horses could drink.

Roads across the Cotswolds followed the ridges, with feeder lanes from the villages in the valleys. Across the clay areas of the Vale the various spreads of river gravels provided the best routeways. The chief problem for roads in the Forest of Dean was the steep gradient around its edge, but there were also many internal valleys to cross. The turnpike trusts also looked at improved and alternative routes. So the steep climb of Birdlip Hill was eased by the use of Crickley Hill, and the treacherous descent through Dowdeswell to Cheltenham was avoided by the new route that skirted Sandywell Park. The most remarkable alternative route was that between Cirencester and Gloucester via Tunley, Bisley, Bull's Cross and Painswick. The 5 mile stone from Cirencester still stands beside the narrow, steep-sided and very muddy bridleway north of Sapperton (77).

The late growth of Cheltenham meant that the turnpikes that were specially built to link it with other towns were established later than those to older settlements, and most date from the early nineteenth century.

77 A section of the alternative road between Cirencester and Gloucester. On the side of this very muddy old road is a stone marked with a 'V'. It is five miles from Cirencester

Travel on these roads by stagecoach averaged 10mph, and the Revd Francis Witts writes in his diary that in 1835 he could leave his rectory in Upper Slaughter after an early breakfast, catch the Oxford coach at Stow at 6am, change coaches in Oxford at 10am and arrive in London at Oxford Street at 4pm.

Two important bridges across the Severn were built by Thomas Telford for the turnpike roads. The Mythe Bridge at Tewkesbury with its toll house was opened in 1826 and Over Bridge at Gloucester was opened in 1832.

Toll roads were not welcomed by all. Welsh cattle drovers on their way to Smithfield tried to avoid them, and the Welshway is one of the alternative routes they used (78). Cattle swam the Severn and then were driven along tracks that avoided the towns and the toll gates. The tracks were wide, with inns at intervals, and the planting of groups of Scots pines marked places where the cattle could stop for the night. The field names 'penny piece' or 'ha'penny piece' refer to the night's grazing charge.

Finally the Parliamentary Enclosure Acts rationalised and fixed the road pattern. Roads were straightened and the boundaries marked by walls and hedges. Widths were standardised and the Acts required widths of 60ft for roads and 40ft for less important lanes. Road surfaces on the Cotswolds were of oolitic limestone, white and dusty in summer, orange and slippery in wet weather. Stone pits were dug beside the roads for these surfacing materials. Much harder stone

78 The Welshway near Bagendon. This was used by cattle drovers on their way to Smithfield. Notice the very wide grass verges

was brought by boat from quarries at Clifton for roads close to the Severn. Local Dolomite was the main material used in the Forest. McAdam surfaces were first used in Bristol but many roads in Gloucestershire were not tarred until the 1930s and some were never improved.

The unimproved roads which have been manured for centuries by passing animals, grazed and trampled, and are often sheltered by old hedges, provide habitats for a rich flora. On the main roads salt, chemical sprays, vehicle exhausts and efficient drainage reduce the wild flower potential of most roadside verges, although recently daffodils have been planted and flower seeds have been scattered along some of the verges.

Thus today's road and lane pattern has a long and complex history, and we have briefly covered the key stages by which the development of the routeways of each parish may be reconstructed. It is sometimes possible to confirm these stages by counting the number of woody species in the hedges that border the roads as outlined in chapter 4. More recent major changes have resulted from the M5 motorway with its junctions for Tewkesbury, Cheltenham, Gloucester and Stroud. This was driven through the county in the late 1960s and opened in 1970. Another improvement has been that of the A417, which became a dual carriageway across the Cotswolds in the early 1990s. Towns which now have bypasses include Cirencester, Lydney, Newent and Northleach, but the continual growth in road traffic ensures that these improvements are merely palliative and bottlenecks occur at rush hour times and in the holiday periods.

Motorists have noticed other visual changes over recent decades. Road signs have increased in their size and frequency, and in many towns they are too numerous to be effective in guiding the motorist. The mileage of double yellow lines has expanded, and in both town and country the majority of the petrol filling stations that spawned in post-war years have closed and their sites have been put to a variety of alternative uses.

We turn now to other modes of transport. As with the much later motorway, the Severn–Thames Canal was planned to serve interests outside the region, and especially to enable bulky goods to be sent from the West Midlands to London. Transport for these goods by water was so much easier and cheaper than by road. The Severn was a free river with no tolls, and was navigable by sea-going ships as far inland as Gloucester at high tide and to small ports downstream at other states of tide. The Wye gave river access upstream and downstream from Lydbrook and Redbrook, and the Thames was navigable from Lechlade, although it was expensive to use because of the large number of tolls at locks and bridges. For other overland water transport, canals were necessary. The first, the Stroudwater Canal, was opened in 1779 to bring coal and wool by Severn trows to the mills along its route (*colour plate 22*). Its extension, forming the Severn–Thames Canal to link the two rivers via the Sapperton tunnel, was opened in 1789. Forty-two locks were necessary to cross the high ground, and for some miles the canal was above the water-table. There was often, therefore, a problem with water supplies. Brimscombe Port was the transshipment point where goods on Severn trows, which were too wide for the tunnel, were moved to Thames barges, which were too long for the Stroudwater locks! Several warehouses and lengthsmen's houses, including five round houses, survive along the sides of the canal which was finally closed in 1933. Its peak trade occurred in 1840 when it carried materials for the construction of the GWR line which followed a roughly similar route.

The towpath may be followed for much of the way and parts of the route are scenic and are havens for wildlife, but nearer to Stroud industrial buildings line the canal. Several short sections have been restored and there are plans to reopen the whole length for leisure use. This, however, entails negotiations with 93 landowners, not all of whom are sympathetic to the proposal!

The Gloucester–Sharpness Canal opened in 1827 after a protracted construction period. Shipping could now avoid the treacherous tidal waters of the Severn and the canal contributed significantly to Gloucester's industrial prosperity. Grain barges supplied the flour mills, timber boats supplied the Moreland match factory and the timber yards, and oil tankers reached the Shell–BP depot at Quedgeley. The nineteenth-century warehouses to store goods for transshipment form a familiar feature of Gloucester's skyline. Nowadays the canal is mainly used for pleasure craft and a boating marina occupies the city docks. A number of swing bridges cross the canal; each has a classical style bridge keeper's house.

Other canals were the Herefordshire–Gloucester Canal, which lasted from 1798 to 1883 when it was replaced by a railway built on parts of the canal. There was also a short feeder canal and wharf at Cambridge. The Combe Hill Canal was opened in 1796 to bring coal and building materials towards Cheltenham. But as transport from Combe Hill to Chester Walk in Cheltenham was by road, the horse-drawn wagons on the Gloucester–Cheltenham plateway, which opened in 1811, could bring coal to Cheltenham more cheaply than by the Combe Hill route, nearly halving the price.

The earliest railways were all plateways for horse-drawn wagons. Iron plates, cast with L-shaped cross-sections in 3ft lengths, were fixed to stone sleepers by an iron spike in an oak plug. Both sleepers and iron rails came from the Forest of Dean and it was here that a network of plateways enabled the transport of coal, iron ore and stone. Two main plateways, or tramroads, crossed the Forest. In the west the Severn–Wye Railway linked Lydbrook and Lydney, and in the east the Bullo Pill Railway connected Churchway Colliery north of Cinderford to the Severn. The many feeder lines from individual mines and quarries to these railways were developed between 1809 and the 1850s. Many of the old plateways may be traced today by following the parallel lines of stone sleepers which were left when the rails were removed (79).

A plateway carried coal from Stratford to Moreton-in-Marsh; Leckhampton quarries were made accessible to Cheltenham builders by a plateway from close to the Devil's Chimney; and there was an unfulfilled plan to extend a plateway to the infamous stone pipe works at the Tally Ho near Hawling. The curves of the line of the Gloucester–Cheltenham plateway are still preserved in the house and property boundaries along its old route in both Gloucester and Cheltenham.

The late 1830s and early 1840s saw the arrival of the steam driven railways. The Birmingham to Gloucester line reached Cheltenham in 1838, and Gloucester's first station for this line was built in 1840. The line from Cheltenham to London via Swindon was opened in stages from 1841. From then on lines spread across the county. Most were single track lines with stations to the design of the particular railway company. The Brunel-style GWR station at Stroud is a rare survivor, and Lansdown Road station in Cheltenham retains some original features. Rail-transported building materials were then used around the stations and these can be seen in houses and bridges today. Coal yards and road carrier services came to these stations and there was stimulation for population growth. Andoversford,

79 The line of an old plateway in the Forest of Dean at Darkhill. Coal was carried along this to the iron works. When the oak trees were planted this was a busy industrial area

80 Andoversford railway junction. One of the last trains leaves on the Kingham line. *Steam Days August 2002: B. J. Ashworth*

with its livestock market, is a good example of a railway settlement at the junction of two late lines crossing the Cotswolds, the Cheltenham to Banbury line and the Midland and Southern Western Junction line to Swindon.

Most of these small lines and their stations closed in 1961 or 1962, and the trains were only carrying a few passengers at the time (*80*). Now the old tracks are used for a variety of purposes including game rearing, light industry, caravan parks and housing. The cuttings and embankments often have geological and botanical interest and in the Forest of Dean and in the Nailsworth valley the lines have been developed as cycle ways for leisure. The Gloucestershire and Warwickshire Railway Company have brought the nostalgia of steam travel back to Toddington on the old Cheltenham–Honeybourne Junction line and there is a similar venture in the Forest between Parkend and Lydney. One wonders at the lost tourism opportunities of a restored Wye Valley line from Ross to Chepstow with stops for Goodrich Castle, Symonds Yat, Monmouth and Tintern Abbey. Generally the disused lines are indicated in our landscape by a narrow band of trees and shrubs which cuts across the pattern of field boundaries in smooth curves.

Thus by this complex network of road and rail, canal and river, people, animals and goods are moved around the county and the routes they take have been largely determined by the desires and requirements of more than 70 generations of previous travellers.

Epilogue

In this book we have reviewed the main elements of the landscape and considered how each has come about. It is relatively easy to analyse a landscape, as we have done in the introduction, and then to follow through a series of studies of its component parts. We have concentrated on the visual aspects and more could be said of the sounds and smells that accompany the views, of the sun and wind on our faces, and of the taste of its produce. But to enjoy the landscape more fully we need to go beyond seeking an understanding of its development. We need time to learn to accept the integrity of each feature, to appreciate the care and skill that have gone into its formation, to have a humble sense of gratitude for it, to reflect on the reasons for its existence and on the conflicts that may be associated with it. Only then will we be able to empathise with the words of the poet Elizabeth Barrett Browning as she looked at the countryside:

> Earth's crammed with heaven,
> And every common bush afire with God;
> But only he who sees takes off his shoes;
> The rest sit round it and pluck blackberries.

Further reading

For the chapters on Goucestershire's geology and geomorphology the two books by William Dreghorn *Geology Explained in the Severn Vale and Cotswolds* 1967 and *Geology Explained in the Forest of Dean and Wye Valley* 1968 are still the most useful, particularly for their block diagrams which show the suggested relationships between the surface and the underlying structures. A detailed study of the Cotswolds with extensive bibiography is *The Geomorphology of the Cotswolds* 1996 by Andrew Goudie and Adrian Parker. For trees and woods Oliver Rackham's *Trees and Woodland in the British Landscape* 1976 is very informative, and for the farming landscape Christopher Taylor's *Fields in the English Landscape* 1975 in the same series is the best introduction. For houses and churches *The Buildings of England – Gloucestershire 1: The Cotswolds* 2000 and *2: The Vale and the Forest of Dean* 2002, both by David Verey and Alan Brooks, are indispensable, not only for their comments on individual buildings but also for their general introductory essays.

Historic Gardens of Gloucestershire 2002 by Timothy Mowl covers in detail all the important stages in garden history that can be traced in the county's gardens. For villages Trevor Rowley's *Villages in the Landscape* 1978 and Brian Roberts' *The Making of the English Village* 1987 give excellent overviews. Much has been written on the towns of the county. Gwen Hart's *A History of Cheltenham* 1981, *Historic Gloucester* 1993 by Philip Moss and *Tewkesbury* 1987 by Anthea

Jones are to be recommended for their detailed coverage. A useful source of information on the county's industrial landscapes is *Exploring Gloucestershire's Industrial Heritage* 2005 by the Gloucestershire Society for Industrial Archaeology. Detailed reference works are *The Industrial History of Dean* 1971 by Cyril Hart and *Gloucestershire Woollen Mills* 1967 by Jennifer Tann.

In *Viewing Gloucestershire* 2006 I examine the responses to the landscape of a selection of earlier writers who, in different ways, attempted to move beyond mere description.

Index

Ordnance Survey grid references for the location of each feature mentioned in the text are given after each entry. Please note: where general reference is made to a village the grid reference is normally to the parish church, otherwise references are to specific features. Page numbers in bold refer to coloured photographs.

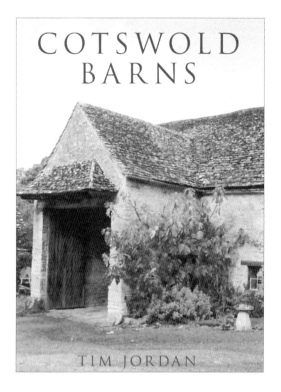

Cotswold Barns
TIM JORDAN

The easily accessible narrative and numerous illustrations in this book help trace the barn's development from the earliest surviving medieval estate and tithe barns, through the growth of the wool trade, to an era where increasing mechanisation changed the life of farming communities, eventually bringing economic depression and leaving the majority of stone barns redundant in today's landscape.

The investigation concludes with a look at the recent revival of barns through their conversion for housing, business, educational and cultural purposes, and with a glossary of the major surviving barns in the area.

0 7524 3740 2

The Textile Industry of South-West England
A Social Archaeology
MARILYN PALMER & PETER NEAVERSON

Splendid buildings like those on the cover of this book are a feature of both townscapes and the countryside in the five counties of Gloucestershire, Wiltshire, Somerset, Dorset and Devon. Yet few people realise they are the legacy of the cloth industry, for which this area was well known in both Britain and Europe from the Middle Ages onwards. Fully illustrated with 100 maps and photographs, a quarter in colour, this book looks at how such buildings help to understand the history of people at work in the past. A final chapter considers the ways in which many of the mills and houses have found new roles in the contemporary landscape.

0 7524 3133 1

Historic Gardens of Gloucestershire

TIMOTHY MOWL

The gardens range from the double-decker cloister entrance of a Plantagenet duke who lost his head because he competed horticulturally with Henry VIII, to a late twentieth-century abstract garden where metal flowers 9ft high weep tears into their own reflections. Painswick Rococo Garden has relics of Pan worship, Warmley a towering clinker giant, Blaise a Picturesque carriage drive by Humphry Repton and Sezincote an Indian stream garden. Dr Timothy Mowl takes the reader around Gloucestershire, discovering what makes it the richest county in England for great gardens of almost every period.

0 7524 1956 0

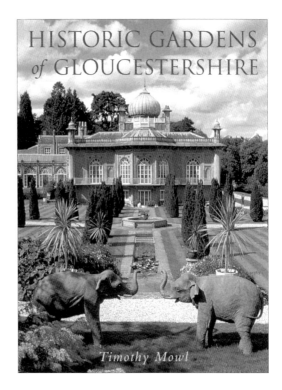

Long Barrows of the Cotswolds

TIMOTHY DARVILL

Long barrows, with their massive tapering mounds and hidden burial chambers, bear witness to the architectural proficiency of our ancestors. Built by early farming communities between 4000 and 3000 BC, they form part of western Europe's earliest surviving architecture. As well as exploring their design, construction and purpose, and the ceremonies that took place at these impressive structures, Professor Darvill examines their origins. their relationships with similar British sites, and shows how they acted as permanent focal points in a changing landscape.

0 7524 2907 8

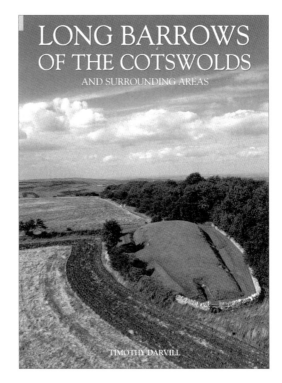